MA1

The information in this book has helped thousands to improve their health, reach personal goals, and grow in mind, body and spirit.

"I really *loved* this book. As a health professional who coaches people regarding diet, exercise and stress management, I certainly will make good use of *Manna for a Modern Age*. It should be required college reading."
— **Sharon Steuer**, M.S.
Certified Hypnotherapist and
Natural Health Counselor

"This book is terrific. Meticulous research, skillful writing, and passionate storytelling make it one of the best books I've read. It makes an important contribution to our understanding of the connections that exist between the mind, body and spirit."
— **Lilia Orlova**, Ph.D.

"A fascinating and unique blend of scientific facts and spiritual revelation. Easy to read, this inspiring book will have a profound impact on anyone who reads it."
— **Martin R. Leopold**, M.D., F.A.C.S.

"As a nurse and facilitator of personal development workshops, I found *Manna for a Modern Age* to contain a wealth of valuable information. One does not put this book away - it remains on the livingroom coffee table for frequent reference. Absolutely inspiring."
— **Anne Brack**, R.N.

"This book is loaded with essential "survival" skills for the 21st century. It's an expression of love in action providing true *manna* to a generation that sorely needs it. We've made this book required reading at the *All Faiths Seminary International*."

- Rabbi Joseph Gelberman,
President of *The All Faiths Seminary International*

"The ideas and strategies in this book will help students to raise their grades and become more successful. But in my opinion, the greater value of this book is that it suggests ways one can become a better human being."

- Maria Ana Usandivaras, college honor student

Larry J. Aufiero, M.S., M.A., is a professor, personal development trainer, seminar leader and co-author of two best-selling college textbooks. He has helped thousands to achieve peak performance and create dynamic, purposeful lives using the time-tested principles in *Manna for a Modern Age*.

MANNA
FOR A
MODERN
AGE

MANNA
FOR A
MODERN
AGE

LARRY AUFIERO

HORIZON PUBLICATIONS
New York, New York

Manna for a Modern Age

Published by: *HORIZON PUBLICATIONS*
New York, New York

Scripture references are from The New American Standard Bible.

Cover design by Robert Aulicino.
Title, subtitle and back cover copy provided by *Susan Kendrick Writing*.

Publisher's -Cataloging In Publication (Provided by Quality Books, Inc.)
Aufiero, Lawrence J.
        Manna for a modern age : essential nourishment for total
        well-being and life-long personal success/ Larry Aufiero. - 1ˢᵗ ed.
p. cm
 Includes index.
 LCCN: 00-26099
 ISBN: 0-9679839-2-4

 1. Success-Religious aspects.
2. Self-actualization (Psychology)
3. Spiritual life. 4. Mind-body
connection   I. Title

BL65.S84A94 2000   158.1
                QBI00-413

Manufactured in the United States of America

TO MY FATHER AND MOTHER

Joseph and *Ann Aufiero*

Thank you for a lifetime of love, guidance and support. On behalf of your children, grandchildren and great grandchildren - we love you deeply.

May our lives always bring honor to your names.

TO MY FAMILY

*My wife **Chris**, who embodies most of what is described in these pages. Thank you for your encouragement and your love. And thank you for picking up the slack within our home when I was too busy to help in the kitchen. I love you.*

*My twin sons **Gabriel** and **Jesse**. It was because of you that I began this project, and it was you who gave me the strength and bullheadedness to continue to the end. Thanks for giving me that proverbial kick in the rear whenever I needed it. Your mother and I are very proud of you.*

*My son **Joseph**. In many ways you have become my teacher. Like your brothers, you have already accomplished great things with your life - I pray that the Lord allows your mother and me the joy of seeing what you do with the rest of it.*

ACKNOWLEDGMENTS

It is with great pleasure and gratitude that I acknowledge the many people whose assistance and encouragement helped make this book a reality. I have been fortunate to have worked with an extraordinary team of publishing professionals, colleagues and friends.

I would like to thank the many who read early drafts of this book and improved it with their comments and suggestions. Although I list them together, each person's contribution is individually appreciated. For their time and attention, I am grateful to: Sharon Steuer, Dr. Suzanne Feldberg, Dennis Stramiello, Dr. Deborah Levine, Kay McKiernan, Ann Marie Pagnotta, Donald Smestad, Grace Miller, Donna Schuller, Dr. Cira Morgillo, Christine Aufiero, Maria Usandivaras, and George Miller.

I am especially indebted to those who made my project their own by providing extensive comments, suggestions, and encouragement:

Sheila Diamondstein - Your excitement over the book and your strong desire to share it with your friends greatly increased my confidence and determination to forge ahead. Thank you.

Dr. Martin Leopold, Dr. Lilia Orlova, Anne Brack, Gene Zirkel, Dr. Jack Dumas - Your exhaustive and expert editing of the book's content and grammatical style is greatly appreciated. The insightful comments you made greatly improved the book's accuracy and readability. As each of you have different backgrounds and professional expertise, your contributions were uniquely valuable.

*****

Marjorie Jones - Editor extraordinare. Your enormous experience in the writing/editing field helped me to make this an infinitely more readable book. I am grateful for your superb editing. Thank you for being sensitive to my time constraints. You were a pleasure to work with.

Gabriel Aufiero - Your brilliant analysis of the book's content coupled with your extraordinary ability to take virtually any text and improve upon it is much appreciated. Thank you for the many hours you devoted to this project - especially since you simultaneously had to contend with your own work-related pressures and responsibilities.

Evelyn Lupardo Masotto - Word processing expert, book designer, and wordsmith of the highest caliber. Your excellent trouble-shooting skills, dedication and perseverance, coupled with your determination to produce a book of the finest quality is greatly appreciated. Because of your style, grace and good humor, you were a joy to work with.

Sharon Castlen - The consummate book marketer. Thank you for providing much helpful advice during the production of this book. Your competence and experience in the field of book production and marketing enabled me to avoid making many mistakes that would have cost me a great deal of time and energy.

Bob Aulicino - When we were searching for an expert in book cover design, your name kept coming up. Now that I've had the pleasure to work with you, I know why you are considered the "consummate" designer. Bob, you did a magnificent job. Thank you.

Susan Kendrick - What can I say? Susan, your faith in this book and its message was a great source of encouragement. Thank you for doing such an outstanding job with the title and back cover copy. Now I understand why you are known as the "best in the field."

Dan Poynter - Your advice concerning writing and publishing was indispensable. Thank you for providing me with expert and timely information - it saved me an enormous amount of time and effort. Your reputation as the guru of book publishing is well deserved.

Charles Colson - I am grateful for your timely words of encouragement and wisdom. They came at just the right time.

Jesse Aufiero - The "computer wizard." Thank you for bailing me out of trouble by solving my recurring computer problems. I am grateful to you for answering all my questions and not making me feel stupid for asking.

Jacob LaPietro - A man whose life and writings have helped me to understand the great and wonderful mysteries of this universe. I am grateful for his wit, wisdom and - most importantly - his walk. His life bore testimony to what one man can accomplish when he surrenders himself to the Almighty One - blessed be His Name.

I love all those who love Me,
and those who diligently seek Me,
shall surely find Me.

- Proverbs 8:17

CONTENTS

PART I

EMPOWERED LIVING

PART II

ANCIENT AFFIRMATIONS

INTRODUCTION

Manna n. 1. (in the Bible) the food miraculously supplied to the Israelites in the wilderness. 2. food for the soul or mind. 3. any necessity unexpectedly supplied.

- Thorndike Barnhart Dictionary

*O*ne act of ignorance can lead to ten thousand acts of ignorance. This occurs when we seek happiness in the wrong places. Most people seek happiness in the external things of life such as wealth, personal appearance, power and popularity; and devalue or ignore the inner attributes of the spirit such as unselfish love, morality and inner strength.

Although self-help and personal development books and programs are helpful, they usually concentrate on the outer qualities of man and omit discussion of the inner qualities. We are basically spiritual beings going through a mental and physical experience. As such, all beneficial and lasting changes must begin on the inside within the human soul.

The information in **Part I** of this book contains easy-to-use strategies and techniques that will help you to reduce stress, reach your goals, and achieve peak performance. The information is based upon studies that are both scientifically and psychologically sound. But more importantly, the material is in harmony with the teachings found in the ancient holy writings - the Bible.

You will be introduced to some of the most recent findings concerning the mind/body connection and learn how the mind, body and *spirit* are all connected. This book represents a blend of science and religion - a confluence of ancient wisdom and modern thinking. Its theme is *empowered living* - the wholesome integration of mind, body and spirit.

It seems unlikely that our Creator would create human life and not provide us with a manual for successful living. I believe He has supplied us with such a book. There is no better blueprint for living than the passages of wisdom within the ancient scriptures. The Bible is the ultimate self-help book. It is God's guidebook to us for survival and optimal living.

While describing the benefits of a life that is balanced in mind, body and spirit, there are no attempts to steer the reader toward any one religion. Ultimately, the spiritual path you decide to walk is a private matter. Only *you* can make the choices and take the actions you feel are the right ones based on the information before you.

Although anecdotal information is used throughout this book, every effort has been made to use sound scientific research to support opinions, assertions and conclusions.

There are 12 chapters in this book. Each one has been designed to take the reader another step toward personal success, self-actualization, and spiritual empowerment. I have had over 25 years experience as an educator - from second grade teacher to college professor - and more than 15 years experience as a personal-development trainer and seminar leader. In that time, I've researched and implemented many strategies and self-help techniques, and made more than a few mistakes along the way. But based on the transformation and progress of many of my students, I believe I have discovered the best and most effective strategies for personal development in existence today. This book will introduce you to them.

It is my sincere hope that this work will provide you with the knowledge and courage you will need to reexamine your life and venture forth into new and uncharted territory - into a place where you no longer are led and controlled solely by the appetites of your mind and body but are instead free to respond to the direction and power of a reawakened spirit.

NOTE: Some of the quotations appearing in this book are anonymous.

✦✦✦✦✦✦✦✦

Part II of this book, **God's Solutions To Your Problems**, contains Bible verses that will lift you up when you are down, inspire you when you feel like quitting, bring inner calm when you are under stress, and help you to choose the proper path as you pursue your purpose. These verses have been grouped by theme for your convenience. For example, when you need courage and inner strength, read the verses listed under the title, *Strength*; when you need guidance, you can turn to the sections titled, *Guidance*, or *Wisdom*. As you read and reflect upon the deeper meaning of the many verses provided, your perspectives will change; you will begin to understand what's really important in life.

I have seen these Bible verses help many of my family members and friends. "Insurmountable" problems somehow become manageable after contemplating the meaning of the words. Every time you read these words, you will benefit - they will provide you with comfort, wisdom, guidance and encouragement. Many feel that they are especially effective when they are read early in the morning as the day begins, and at night just before bed time.

As you immerse yourself in these verses, any guilt, anger or fear that may be hindering your progress will begin to fade. Once this happens, there is often a dramatic improvement in health - both physical and emotional. These verses will also give you reasons to look forward to the excitement and promise of each new day. When you have renewed hope within a nourished spirit, it is easier to be excited about simply being alive.

PART I

EMPOWERED LIVING

Are you in earnest? Seize this very minute! Boldness has genius, power and magic in it. Only engage, and then the mind grows heated. Begin, and then the work will be completed.
-John Anster

Call to Me, and I will answer you, and I will tell you great and mighty things, which you do not know.
- Jeremiah 33:3

PART I

ENDODERIVOSO

1

THE MIND/BODY CONNECTION

The heights by great men reached and kept were not attained by sudden flight. But they, while their companions slept, were toiling upward in the night.
- Henry Wadsworth Longfellow

It takes more stress and poison to kill someone who has peace of mind and loves life.
- Dr. Bernie Siegel

This is an exciting time to be alive. Recent discoveries have begun to demonstrate the fascinating link between mind and body. As you learn to make positive changes in one, you will make positive changes in the other. As you monitor and control your thought patterns and the way you view life, you will improve your health and approach peak performance. What goes on in the mind affects the body. When you are angry, sad, lonely or frightened - your body cells know it and suffer in some way. And when you experience joy, your cells rejoice with you.

Just as our thoughts affect our physical state, our thought patterns strongly affect our ability to accomplish the goals we set. We begin by learning how our thoughts influence each of our actions.

The Power of the Mind

There is a principle that has been discovered within the field of *cognitive psychology* that is so powerful that it can change your life. Simply put, *we become what we think about*. That is, we tend to move toward our dominant thoughts.

If there's something you want to accomplish, think about it often throughout the day. If you want to lose a bad habit and replace it with a good one, begin to see yourself in possession of the new habit. Visualize yourself acting in the desired way and you will greatly improve the likelihood of acquiring the new habit. That which you dwell upon will tend to manifest itself in your life.

The biographies of famous people are replete with stories that exemplify this principle. Starting at an early age, many of the heros and heroines of this world formed an image in their minds of the kinds of people they wanted to become and never let go of that image. How would you like your life to unfold? Get a vivid picture of what you want to accomplish and the person you want to become; hold that picture in your mind throughout the day. Let your mind bask in the warmth of your hopes and dreams. As you dwell upon the picture of your world as you would like it to be and seek God's counsel, you will inexorably move toward it.

In some ways, the act of prayer is one example of this psychological phenomenon. When you consistently pray for something, you are directing your mind to dwell upon that which you want to see happen.

Prayer may or may not change God's actions - that's up to God; but it *will* change the one who prays. After you pray, you will somehow feel better - hope will replace hopelessness. A sense of inner peace will begin to replace anxiety and fear.

The idea that we move toward that which we dwell upon is closely associated with the concept of *positive thinking*. Positive thinking refers to the process of holding positive, life affirming thoughts in the mind.

These favorable thoughts trigger images which create positive attitudes and emotions. For this reason, positive thinking is a powerful tool for goal achievement. By constantly thinking about your goal and seeing yourself in possession of it, positive thinking will heighten your expectations and help you to reach that goal.

> *There is a law in psychology that if you form a picture in your mind of what you would like to be, and you keep and you hold that picture there long enough, you will soon become exactly as you have been thinking.*
>
> - William James

You Become What You Do

We have seen that people can achieve great things once they believe that they can. But the chain reaction that takes place between our thoughts and our behavior is reversible. Psychologists tell us that not only do we tend to become what we dwell upon, but we come to believe that which we do. Your actions strongly influence your feelings and your beliefs. The way you live your life has a strong impact on how you come to view life. What you do (whether you like it or not) will shape what you come to believe and how you feel. Act nobly, do the right thing - even if at first you are uncomfortable doing it - and before very long, you'll become comfortable doing it.

I have a friend who is admired and respected by virtually all who know her. Approaching 60 years of age, this energetic woman almost always seems to have a positive outlook and demonstrates sincere concern for other people. Her cheerful demeanor usually rubs off on the people who come into contact with her. Someone once asked her, "It must be great to wake up each day feeling good about yourself and your place in the world. What's your secret?"

Our friend told us, "Oh, you would be surprised to know that I usually don't wake up feeling so great. Often, my body hurts and my thoughts gravitate to all my concerns and problems. But I face each day grateful for what I have and I make up my mind to be happy. I look for ways to perform what I call random acts of kindness. As soon as I get up and at 'em each day, I start acting like I'm the luckiest person to be alive and before very long that's just how I feel."

Fake It Until You Make It

Knowing that your actions strongly influence your belief system can be a powerful tool for inner growth and peak performance. If, for example, you don't feel like going out and socializing, but you go anyway and *act* as though you're glad to see everyone and you *act* as though you're having a good time, soon you will feel the way you're acting. You'll start to feel good and you'll probably have a great time! In short, you tend to become what you do.

Immature people let their feelings rule. As we mature, we learn to do what is right and let our feelings catch up. This technique is called *"fake it until you make it."* If you act the way you want to feel, soon you will feel the way you are acting.

Good intentions are important, but in themselves mean little. Right conduct, even when not accompanied by a willing heart, will ultimately inspire the proper motives as well.

How to "Act As If"

Years ago - soon after graduating from college - I was working in New York City as a computer programmer/analyst. At that time, I volunteered to teach at *Phoenix House*, a drug-rehabilitation center. My assignment was to help the residents pass their high school equivalency exam. As my students filed in, I became so nervous and "up-tight" that I couldn't speak. I was actually about to walk out of the room when a counselor who worked there, sensing my fear, came over, took me aside and quietly told me to "just fake it."

He explained how he had the same reaction the first time he was about to instruct a group of people. Instead of running, he forced himself to act and speak as if he were the most confident and competent teacher alive. He explained how, after a few minutes of faking it, he was calmly, confidently and convincingly teaching his students. He pulled it off. You can imagine my delight when I took his advice that day and it worked for me. Since that time, I've used this technique on many occasions.

The next time you are facing a difficult challenge - one you feel incapable of accomplishing - just "act as if" you can do it, and you probably will. Also, it will help enormously if you silently repeat this mantra to yourself just before you take that first courageous step: "*Oh, what the heck, I'll go for it anyway.*" This little phrase will remind you that in most instances, you really have nothing to lose. So, the next time you are about to run away from a challenge because you feel you don't have what it takes, just take a deep breath and *go for it anyway*.

Setting your mind on what you want to see happen in your life is an example of positive thinking. But contrary to what has been advertised, positive thinking is not so easy to accomplish.

The Problem With Positive Thinking

Obviously, positive thinking can never guarantee that you will get what you want. It doesn't matter how much you believe you can flap your arms and fly like a bird - it just isn't going to happen. However, positive thinking will let you do everything better than negative thinking will.

Unfortunately, positive thinking can be difficult. Psychologists tell us that most people think negative thoughts a large portion of the time. It would be wonderful if we could bring optimistic, loving, joy-filled thoughts into our consciousness at will. If we could, we would find it easier to be happy and achieve our goals.

The problem with positive thinking is we simply can't do it on command - reality gets in the way. When we are depressed or anxious about something, it is often difficult or close to impossible to think positively. Fortunately, there are techniques that will help you to think positively. One of them involves the use of affirmations and visualization.

Affirmations

The dominant thoughts which we hold in our mind seek expression in outward physical action. Accordingly, any goal that you persistently hold in your mind will seek expression through some practical means. As you concentrate on the person you intend to become, and hold that image in your mind, you will slowly and naturally become that person.

A useful strategy for holding your goals in your mind is the use of *affirmations*. An affirmation is a statement of a goal that is written in the present, and is personal and positive. For example, if one of your goals is to improve the way you relate to people, so that you treat people with more respect, your affirmation might be: *"It's such a good feeling to know that I treat people with the kindness and consideration they deserve."* In other words, you begin to control your "self-talk," that constant conversation you are always having with yourself.

If your goal is to lose 25 pounds by a certain date, you could write your affirmation this way: *"I'm so happy now that I weigh 158 pounds; I have plenty of energy and I feel great."* By writing the affirmation in the present, as if it's already accomplished, it becomes more effective. Affirmations can be written on several index cards and left in places where you could read them throughout the day: on the night stand next to your bed, posted on the bathroom mirror, taped to your dashboard, on the kitchen table, on your desk, etc.

The most effective times to read your affirmations are upon rising in the morning and just before going to sleep at night. You can have a different affirmation for each of your goals.

Reading the Bible verses that are in the second half of this book will engage your mind in much the same way affirmations do; they allow you to focus upon that which you desire. For example, within the section titled *Hope*, we find the following:

And let us not lose heart in doing good, for in due time, we shall reap if we do not grow weary.
                                        - Galatians:6:9

A mind centered on this truth will experience hope, strength and determination. When all seems dark and hopeless, when you are about to give up, meditating on this verse will provide you with resilience and courage. It will empower you to stay the course no matter how difficult the struggle.

Visualization

After reading one of your affirmations you should then close your eyes and *visualize* yourself being what you want to be, or doing what it is you desire to do. Using the example of losing weight, you might visualize yourself looking healthier, happier and more vibrant at your desired weight.

You can use affirmations and visualization for *any* goal: to help heal your body, improve your golf game, remain calm and confident during an exam, excel on a job interview, or become a more patient, loving person. For years now, sports psychologists have been teaching visualization techniques to athletes with extraordinary results.

Repeating this process several times a day for a few days or for several weeks will cause your subconscious to accept your goal statement as truth. Your self-image will slowly change until you see yourself as a fit person. Then, when you step on the scale, and reality (your actual weight) does not match up with your new image of yourself, you have a problem. And this self created problem is what you want. It's going to motivate you to achieve that which you desire.

Until you change and make the outside (reality) match up with the inside picture, you will experience tension and discomfort. This uneasiness occurs whenever we believe something about ourselves but behave in a contradictory manner. You have intentionally created an inner conflict - a conflict that will both annoy and motivate you until you resolve it.

A Remarkable Success Story

After learning of this affirm-and-visualize technique, one of my math students decided to give it the ol' college try and had spectacular results.

A twenty-year-old student, I will call her Gail, set three goals for herself. The first two were somewhat related in that they pertained to her appearance and her health. Her first goal was to lose 14 pounds and the second was to stop smoking. At the time, our country was at war with Iraq, and her fiancé was involved in Operation Desert Storm. Since her fiancé was scheduled to come home in five months, she wanted to accomplish both goals by May 1 of that year.

As instructed, she wrote her affirmations for these two goals on 3x5 index cards and placed the cards in places where she would see them throughout the day: on her night stand, attached to the medicine cabinet, in her car, on the kitchen table, in her book bag and in some of her textbooks. When possible, after reading each affirmation, Gail would close her eyes and visualize herself in possession of her goals.

She started by reading her first affirmation, "I am so happy, now that I weigh 140 pounds. I feel great!" Then she closed her eyes and *visualized* herself wearing her favorite blue dress (one she hadn't been able to wear for over a year) and greeting her fiancé upon his return from the Gulf War.

Next, she read her second affirmation, "I am so proud of myself now that I am a nonsmoker." Then she'd close her eyes and imagine herself running along the shore of the Atlantic Ocean enjoying the warmth from the sun and having the lung capacity needed to run long distances.

By doing this throughout the day, every day, for several months, Gail gradually and naturally changed her self-image in those areas. Eventually, she no longer saw herself as a smoker and she no longer had an image of herself as overweight. Every time she would light up a cigarette she felt uneasy and frustrated with her behavior. "Incredibly," she explained, "my enjoyment for smoking decreased with every cigarette I smoked."

Whenever she opened her refrigerator, her eyes were no longer drawn to the cake that was sitting there. Miraculously, the fruits and vegetables began to look more and more appealing. Imagine!

During final-exam week, Gail announced to a surprised but delighted class that she had lost 18 pounds (it was obvious to all that she had indeed lost the weight) and that she had not smoked a cigarette in four weeks. Furthermore, she lost the desire to have a cigarette.

This success story doesn't end here. Gail's third goal was to work hard and get a high grade. Yes, Gail earned an **A** for the course. It is true, we do indeed move toward that which we think about all day long.

This technique is not magic. It doesn't work every time with every person. Still, I have seen dozens of students, athletes, and others use this technique to improve relationships, overcome problems, rid themselves of bad habits, and reach a great variety of personal goals. Some things have to be believed to be seen. Believe first, then act, and soon you will see it accomplished.

Once you imagine, affirm, and visualize your goal, your subconscious mind begins to go to work for you.

The Power of the Subconscious Mind

Your subconscious has incredible power. It is designed to creatively resolve mental conflicts and will work on them day and night - even when you are asleep. Thomas Edison, arguably the world's greatest inventor, took several naps throughout the day in order to tap into the power of his subconscious. By using this technique, he overcame obstacles and solved many problems that stood in the way of his many remarkable accomplishments.

In a similar manner, your subconscious can be used to solve your problems. Specifically, it will struggle with your self created dilemmas until the outside matches the inside.

Since meaningful and lasting change usually begins on the inside and works its way outward, if you persistently hold your affirmation and the image it produces in your mind, your creative subconscious will begin an amazing process. It will automatically provide you with extraordinarily creative ideas, insights and programs for change. In addition, it will also give you an intense desire to achieve your goal.

Success

Before giving you the formula for success, we must agree on what we mean by that word. There are many aspects to being successful in life. Being successful is an ongoing process - it is a journey, not a destination.

To enjoy high levels of health and vitality, to have loving relationships - with God, family and friends, to experience the progressive realization of a worthy goal, to have an abundance of that which brings lasting joy, to experience a quiet inner peace - regardless of outer circumstances, to know that we have helped to make this world a better place because the gifts we gave to others and society outnumbered the gifts we received from them - this, I believe, is what constitutes a successful life.

Success means we go to sleep at night knowing that our talents and abilities were used in a way that served others.

- Marianne Williamson

The Formula for Success

* Set Goals - Success has much to do with setting worthy goals and then achieving them. A clear, well-defined goal acts as a magnet that pulls you to itself. When you start the process of setting goals and using affirmations and visualization, you don't have to concern yourself with how you're going to proceed. Just hold the goal firmly in your mind. How will it look when you achieve it? Can you see it? Remind yourself why you want what you want. If you are passionate about the reasons *why*, you will find the *how*.

> *If one advances confidently in the direction of his dreams, and endeavors to live the life which he has imagined, he will meet with a success unexpected in common hours.*
>
> - Henry David Thoreau

* Act - As you continue to affirm, visualize and seek divine guidance, the steps to your goal will eventually come to you. And when they do, don't hesitate - act. Getting started is often difficult. The first step is usually the hardest. To complicate matters, you may have a tendency to procrastinate. You may procrastinate by doing nothing, or you may get involved in actions that have nothing to do with your goal.

The best way to overcome this tendency is to *do something* that will move you forward, no matter how ridiculous it seems. Take a small portion of the task in front of you and get started. Usually, by completing a small piece of the whole, you will break the state of inertia.

Things may come to those who wait, but only those things left by those who hustle.

- Abraham Lincoln

* Expect Setbacks - Don't worry about failing. Studies of high-achievers show that whereas most people do not realize their full potential because they're afraid of failing, high-achievers treat each "failure" as an "outcome" and a learning experience. Each outcome, they understand, takes them one step closer to their goal. Usually, it's impossible to succeed at something without making mistakes and "failing." If you've never fallen, you've never climbed; if you've never stumbled, you've never soared.

I'm not a good shot, but I shoot often.
- Theodore Roosevelt

The greatest accomplishment is not in never failing, but in rising again after you fall.
- Vince Lombardi

* Use Feedback - Once you set your course and begin your quest, learn all you can about the subject at hand. As you act, study the results of your actions, be open to feedback - use what works and discard what doesn't.

* Model Success - Seek out the people who excel in the area in which you are involved. Model their behavior whenever and wherever it's appropriate. Modeling the behavior of winners and people of excellence will get you to your goal faster and with less effort.

* **Ask For Help** - Make a habit of *asking* for what you want. Posing the right questions to the right people will save you an enormous amount of time in achieving your goals. Once you contact the specialists and experts in your field of interest, sit at their feet and learn from them. If necessary, pay for their services. It will be well worth it. When attempting to go from point A to point B it is imperative that you learn to ask, ask, ask for help and directions. One of the most important phrases you could ever learn is "Excuse me, can you help me please?"

When the student is ready, the teacher will appear.

Dr. Bernie Siegel is the world renowned, best-selling author of *Love, Medicine and Miracles* and other outstanding books pertaining to personal empowerment. I phoned Dr. Siegel and asked if he would like to read my manuscript and perhaps send an endorsement. Sounding weary, he said, "I'd like to help you but I don't do that any longer. I'm just too busy with my own work - I'm sorry." I told him that I understood and wished him well.

After thinking about it for a few days, I decided to send the manuscript to Dr. Siegel with a letter. In part, the letter explained that I was convinced that he would find value in the book. I said that if he did not have the time to read the manuscript in the weeks ahead he could give it to a friend or loved one who might enjoy it.

When I was ready to go to the post office with the manuscript, I asked my twin sons, Gabriel and Jesse to put their hands on it. I said a short prayer. "Lord, please let Dr. Siegel read this manuscript. If he finds some value in it, I ask that he write a little endorsement for it." We all said a hearty "Amen!" and I went off to mail my work.

Several weeks later, I received a letter from Doctor Siegel. Not only had he read the manuscript, but he liked it! He graciously sent me a beautiful note of encouragement along with the endorsement that appears on the back cover of this book. His only advice to me was to include more stories in the book - "Anecdotes will add inspiration to your information." (I took Dr. Siegel's advice and added a few more anecdotes. The story you just read was added to the manuscript with his permission.) Never be afraid to ask for help. But more important, always be ready to offer help to those who truly need it.

> *Ask, and it shall be given unto you; seek, and you shall find; knock and it shall be opened to you.*
> - Luke 11:9

* Help Others Become Successful - Some of you might be familiar with the biblical saying, "For whatever a man sows, this he will also reap." When you plant good seeds - by doing good deeds and bringing assistance and success to others - those seeds will one day bear fruit in your life. This is an example of the *law of cause and effect*.

Good fortune and success have a way of embracing the

one who makes a habit of helping others. I have seen the manifestation of this law many, many times in my life and in the lives of others. We indeed reap what we sow. Give comfort to others and you will receive comfort. Be available to give of your time, energy, and resources, and you will receive in kind.

Give, and it will be given to you; good measure, pressed down, shaken together, running over, they will pour into your lap. For whatever you deal out to others, it will be dealt to you in return.
                                        - Luke 6:38

* Stay the Course - When you begin a project, you must expect to encounter frustrations, obstacles, and walls that will seem impenetrable. At times, you will hear that nagging inner voice of self-doubt giving you all these great reasons why you should give up. You might even wonder why you ever believed you could accomplish the task in the first place. Don't believe this negative harbinger of doom. When it comes and brings doubt and fear, simply stay the course.

Winners are people who get up one more time. Quitters never win and winners never quit. It's okay to fall down, but it's not okay to stay down. Feelings can be deceiving. Our moods can deceive us. You may *feel* that all is lost and that you will never cross that finish line, but in reality, you may be doing fine. Just carry on.

The successful person is the one who forms the habit of doing what the unsuccessful person hates to do.
                                        - Donald Riggs

Never give up, never give up, never, never, never, never - in nothing great or small, large or petty - never give in except to convictions of honor and good sense.   - Winston Churchill

* Be Prepared to Fight - I have never seen this ingredient included in any other recipe for success but I am convinced that it is essential. An alternative title for this step to success might be - *Make Peace Not War, But Be Prepared for Both.* Obviously, you should seek to be kind, considerate, supportive and loving. But there will be times when being too eager to please others will prevent you from accomplishing great things with your life. There will be times when being docile or acquiescent will be counterproductive - not only for you, but also for the world around you.

When Hitler's troops rounded up and deported Jews and others of "inferior blood," most of the German population simply looked the other way and did nothing. Their acquiescence enabled Hitler to accomplish the evil he set out to do. This begs the question - "How many times have *we* stood by and done nothing when we should have acted?" Even those great martyrs for peace - Mahatma Ghandi and Martin Luther King Jr.- knew when it was time to stop being "Mr. Nice Guy." Their passive resistance movements succeeded only because they were tough. They knew when it was time to fight - not with weapons of destruction, but with organized resistance.

All it takes for evil to triumph is for good men to do nothing.   - Edmund Burke

I grew up in East New York - a tough section of Brooklyn, New York. In those days, I was not aggressive. In fact, I hated to fight. But unfortunately for me, being a congenial little six-year-old would not describe most of the other kids in my neighborhood. One kid in particular - I'll call him Duke - loved to beat up people. He was the toughest kid in the neighborhood and the undisputed "leader." Since Duke took special joy in using me as a punching bag, I was terrified of him. My mother was tired of washing my torn and bloodied tee shirts. My father was tired of being known as "the father of the fat kid who is always getting the crap knocked out of him." I hated going to school each day because Duke prowled the halls and school yard looking for prey - often *me*! No matter how nice I tried to be to this guy, he found a way to make my life miserable. After school, I usually stayed in my house and watched as the other kids played outside. To say that I was not a happy camper would be an understatement.

One day, my father came home from work with a pair of boxing gloves and told me that I had to learn how to fight. He marched me down into the basement, and my boxing lessons began. Several weeks later, to everyone's surprise, I walked up to Duke and told him that I wanted to fight him the next day. (I don't think anyone noticed my knees shaking, but I couldn't be sure.)

The day of the big fight was something to behold. It was like a three-ring circus had rolled into town. When I got to the spot where we agreed to fight, there were more than ten boys my age and a few teens waiting there - all anxious to see a little blood. When we finally went at it, something snapped inside of me. I became a different person. Although I was getting hit hard about my face and body, I never felt a thing. I had this wonderful feeling of being at peace. Later, I realized that this liberated feeling was nothing more than the absence of fear. Being proactive rather than reactive gave me a feeling of strength and self-respect I had never known before. After about three minutes of wild swinging (it seemed more like three hundred), one of the older boys asked if either of us wanted to stop. I was about to yell, "Yeah, I do!" when Duke shouted, *"I'll stop if you will!"* Those five words were the sweetest words I had heard up to that point in my short but turbulent life.

From that moment on, my world changed dramatically. I was a different person. I began to like myself. Duke and I entered a state of peaceful coexistence. He actually told me that he wanted me to be his "helper." (What an honor.)

I learned some important lessons from this episode in my life. I learned that there are some people in this world who will return your affection with a slap in the face, and will return your slap with an embrace. Also, there will be times in all of our lives when we will have to fight for what is right. The alternative - capitulation - just doesn't work. Evil that goes unchecked can only grow. On a related note, if you have a noble goal, know this: sooner or later you will encounter resistance. And the greater your goal, the greater the resistance will be. How you face up to that resistance will determine your success - both social and spiritual. When faced with a seemingly insurmountable obstacle, do all you can to prepare - then act!

✦✦✦✦✦✦✦✦

Your thought patterns not only affect your ability to achieve your goals and become successful, they also have a direct effect on your health.

How Your Thought Patterns Influence Your Health

Scientific data has shown that our thoughts generate emotions, and the emotions we feel produce special chemicals, such as neuropeptides, neurotransmitters, and endocrine secretions. Peptides are primarily amino acids - the building blocks of protein. These chemicals act as messengers and attach themselves to receptors which have been found not only in the brain, but in the immune system and other parts of the body as well.

The messenger molecules and their receptors allow various systems of the body to actually communicate with each other. For example, if you are afraid of something, every time you think about that "something," you will manufacture "fearful" chemicals that will communicate the fear to the receptors in other places like your stomach (I had a knot in the pit of my stomach), your heart (I became fainthearted), or your respiratory system (I was scared breathless). Living with constant fear - or *any* negative emotion for that matter - will exact a heavy toll on your health.

A Natural High

Candace Pert, Ph.D., a professor at the Center for Molecular and Behavioral Neuroscience at Rutgers University, discovered ways to measure the receptors in the brain that receive opiates like opium, heroin, and codeine. Later, it was found that the brain makes its own morphine-like chemicals called *endorphins*, shorthand for "endogenous morphines." These "happy," or pain-relieving chemicals are created by highly positive emotions. Endorphins are also produced by sustained aerobic exercise. This is why so many people feel exhilarated after a good aerobic workout.

Your mind has the capacity to produce a variety of wonderfully healing, life-empowering drugs. Why take a pain-killer, which only masks the pain of a headache, when dwelling on the right thoughts could, in many cases, bring about the appropriate emotions to produce the ideal chemicals that would eliminate the headache pain altogether?

There are some who suffer from depression caused by a chemical imbalance in the brain. They should consult a mental health professional who would probably recommend a combination of antidepressants and therapy. Learning to help ourselves to become healthier does not mean that we ignore help from the medical community.

Your brain produces a chemical that relays the news of your happiness to all 52 million of your body cells - who rejoice and join in.

- Deepak Chopra

What You Believe Is What You Will See

Our thought patterns do more than affect our feelings. If you begin with your thoughts, you can trace the effect your thoughts and beliefs have on your behavior:

1. Your beliefs affect your **expectations**.
2. Expectations affect your **emotions**.
3. Emotions affect your **attitudes**.
4. Attitudes affect your **performance.**

If you want your performance to be outstanding, start with the way you perceive things. As much as possible, keep your thoughts positive. As you learn and practice the strategies for excellence that are presented in this book, you can be optimistic about your ability to reach whatever realistic goal you set for yourself.

To reiterate, your thought patterns not only affect your performance, your thinking also has a direct impact on your health. Statisticians who study mortality rates and the cause of illness tell us that more people die on a Sunday night than at any other time of the week. They believe it is because most people are not exactly thrilled about the prospect of beginning another week. Apparently, many working people hate their jobs. Sometimes, those who are retired and living alone do not look forward to the loneliness that the week days can bring. If you know of someone who may be alone or lonely, today may be a good time to call them.

Nothing demonstrates the mind/body connection more dramatically than the *placebo effect*.

The Placebo - a Mind/Body Connector

Placebo, Latin for "I shall please," is a medical treatment that is devoid of any active medication. It is a "lie that heals." The mysterious nature of the placebo effect has mystified the medical profession ever since it was first detected several decades ago.

One of the most incredible examples of the placebo response occurred in 1957. A patient, we will call him Mr. Jones, was found to have cancerous tumors the size of oranges and was given just days to live. Hospitalized in Long Beach, California, he heard that a horse serum, Krebiozen, might be effective against cancer and begged his doctor to let him receive it.

One afternoon, his doctor, Philip West, relented and gave Mr. Jones an injection. Within a very short time, to the astonishment of his physician and the hospital staff, Mr. Jones made a startling recovery. In just a few days he was off his "death bed" and out of the hospital. The tumors, wrote Dr. West, "had melted like snowballs on a stove."

Two months later, Mr. Jones read medical reports stating that the horse serum was not an effective treatment against cancer. Within days the tumors returned, he suffered a complete relapse and was again hospitalized.

Dr. West told his patient that he obtained "a new super-refined, double-strength" version of the drug and injected him with it. Actually, the injections were nothing more than sterile water. As before, the tumors melted and he went home and resumed a normal life. Our Mr. Jones was the "picture of health" and symptom-free for over two months.

Then one day Mr. Jones read a definitive report written by the American Medical Association regarding this drug: "Nationwide tests show Krebiozen to be a worthless drug in the treatment of cancer." The tumors returned. Within a few days, Mr. Jones was dead.

Hope Can Heal While Fear Destroys

Apparently, the patient's faith in his doctor and the serum

brought about his remarkable recovery. He expected to get better and he did. Unfortunately, the *nocebo effect* also came into play. A nocebo is a negative belief which has adverse effects on one's health and performance. When Mr. Jones believed that the serum was worthless, his body responded accordingly. In both instances, it was the mind that had a direct and startling effect on the body.

The late Dr. Henry Beecher, an anesthesiologist at Harvard, has conducted extensive studies regarding the effectiveness of placebos. He discovered through multiple studies involving 1,082 patients, that 35 percent of patients experienced "satisfactory relief" when placebos were used instead of regular medication for a wide range of medical problems. In a related study, when a group of patients was given a placebo in place of an antihistamine, 77 percent reported drowsiness - a side effect of antihistamines.

Positive Expectations Lead to Positive Results

A relatively new field within cognitive psychology (the study of how our thought patterns affect our behavior) known as *expectancy theory* attempts to explain how the placebo effect works. Research has shown that our beliefs affect the hormones we produce, which in turn affect our immune system.

A positive belief such as "I know I am going to get well," will create health-enhancing hormones which enter your bloodstream and strengthen your immune system. Similarly, if you believe "I am not going to survive this," the resultant anxiety and fear will produce "stress" hormones that will weaken your immune system.

Your beliefs control your expectations, which influence not only your health, but your behavior as well. When you expect to heal or succeed in some endeavor, you put yourself in a better position to do just that.

The physician's behavior and enthusiasm for the "medicine" being administered has a lot to do with the success of the treatment. If Dr. Lowkey says, "I don't know if this drug will work, but let's give it a try," and Dr. Upbeat enthusiastically tells her patient, "This is a powerful drug that has had a wonderful track record," studies have shown that Dr. Upbeat's patients will be back on their feet long before Dr. Lowkey's will.

The Amazing Power of Hope

As a professor, I do all I can to convince my students that if they work hard I expect them to do well in my class. And usually they do. A good parent is one who makes children realize that they have more ability than they exhibit, so they consistently do better than they thought they could. A good boss will do the same. Not only doctors, parents, and teachers but *any* person in a position to influence another, can be a powerful agent for optimism and hope. And hope, as we have seen, can lead to positive expectations and some pretty amazing results.

The placebo response proves that there is no real separation between the body and the mind. Your thought patterns will either help you or harm you. In extreme cases, they can either heal or destroy. The intent of this book is to introduce you to insights and strategies that will help you to develop and habituate positive, life-enhancing patterns of thinking and behaving.

The Mind/Body Connection

This mind/body interaction can begin in the mind and affect the body or it can begin in the body and affect the mind (for example, a relaxing body massage). The conduit for this interaction is the bloodstream.

> *The life of the body is in the blood.*
> - Leviticus 17:11

Laugh - It's Good for You

One of the most celebrated stories concerning a patient's recovery from a disease is that of Norman Cousins' remarkable recovery from a crippling and near-fatal illness. In his book *Anatomy of an Illness*, Cousins, author and one-time editor of the *Saturday Review* magazine, describes how he used laughter and his body's own natural healing powers to gain victory over a near incurable sickness.

Cousins contracted a serious collagen disease that was destroying his connective tissue. He experienced excruciating pain and had great trouble moving his body. When he was told by his doctors that he had one chance in five hundred of recovering, he decided to take charge of certain aspects of his treatment.

Knowing about the placebo and the nocebo effects, Cousins was convinced that positive emotions, such as love, hope, faith, laughter, confidence and the will to live, all have powerful therapeutic value. He believed he could enlist his body's natural healing resources to get well again. With the full cooperation of his physician, Cousins checked himself out of the hospital and into a hotel room where he arranged a more cheerful and comfortable environment for himself.

Humor Therapy

Cousins credits his miraculous recovery to visualization, the love of his friends and family, and humor therapy. (He also ate a nutritious diet and took megadoses of vitamin C.) In an effort to reduce the excruciating pain, he watched Marx Brothers movies and "Candid Camera" films; he also read humor books.

The experiment worked. His doctor and nurse were astonished to find that ten minutes of genuine belly laughter had an anesthetic effect and gave him at least two hours of pain-free sleep.

They also discovered that each laugh session was followed by a reduction in inflammation which was both measurable and cumulative. Cousins was ecstatic. Indeed, all the evidence confirmed the ancient theory that "laughter is the best medicine."

Norman Cousins recovered fully and went on to live a normal, healthy and productive life. Against all odds, he won his battle. Humor, it seems, is the miracle drug with no bad side effects. Having a good sense of humor does not necessarily mean that you are a good teller of jokes. It means you have the ability to find humor in much of what happens to you in the normal course of the day. It's also important that you have the ability to laugh at yourself. Learn to see the funny side as well as the serious aspects to your problems. Don't take yourself so seriously - remember, he who laughs....lasts.

Blessed is he who has learned to laugh at himself,
for he shall never cease to be entertained.
                                        - John Boswell

*Laughter is the greatest weapon we have and the one
we use the least.*   -Mark Twain

Laughter's Health Benefits

Dr. William Fry, M.D., a clinical professor at Stanford
University Medical School, has been investigating the benefits
of humor on health for more than twenty-eight years. His
findings indicate that mirth and laughter have definite physical
benefits. Laughter:

* Stimulates the entire circulatory system. By
  exercising the diaphragm, laughter benefits the
  cardiovascular system and increases the oxygen
  in the blood. Twenty seconds of laughter
  produces the same cardiovascular benefits as 3
  minutes of exercise.
* Reduces the heart rate and lowers blood pressure.
* Reduces inflammation.
* Reduces muscle tension.
* Fights depression and anxiety.
* Helps the healing process.
* Reduces pain. A good laughing session will not
  only distract us, but will also increase production
  of *endorphins* - the body's natural pain killers.
* Boosts immune function. As the diaphragm is
  exercised, the lymphatic system improves; this,
  in turn, allows us to fight infections, viruses, and
  other dangerous internal invaders.

* Stimulates the creative process. Fun and laughter seem to release the mind's creative juices. As a result, more and more companies are scheduling regular fun-and-laughter sessions in order to come up with innovative money-making ideas.

If you're sick, laughter will help you to get well. If you're well, laughing will help you to feel even better. Mirth is sometimes better than medicine. It doesn't matter if you feel like laughing or not, just the act of laughing is what heals and energizes. Take time to laugh, it is the music of the soul. So what are you waiting for? Laugh!

Here is a small sample of the wisdom of that inimitable philosopher, Yogi Berra:

* *When you come to a fork in the road, take it.*
* *Always go to other people's funerals, otherwise they won't go to yours.*
* *Never answer an anonymous letter.*
* *No one goes there anymore, it's too crowded.*
* *I didn't say everything I said.*

Smile, It's Good for You

Your emotions affect your physiology. When you are sad or anxious, your tone of voice, posture, walk, and breathing will all be affected. But it also works the other way - your physiology is always telling your mind and heart how you are feeling.

By taking control of certain aspects of your physiology, you will begin to take control of your emotions. Singing, whistling, and walking with a "bounce" in your step will help you to feel better. It has been said that it's very difficult to walk fast and feel bad at the same time. Laugh or smile, even when you don't feel like it, and soon your heart will respond in kind; you might even find yourself laughing from the joy bubbling up within you. It is almost impossible to smile on the outside without feeling better on the inside.

This interaction between body and mind is one of the reasons that a good massage helps us to feel better psychologically.

The Magic of Touch

The *Touch Research Institute* (TRI) in Miami is the only scientific institute in the world established for the sole purpose of studying the effects of touch and massage on health. A few years ago, TRI psychologist Tiffany Field and her staff, in collaboration with researchers at the University of Miami and Harvard University, conducted a series of studies the results of which were nothing short of astounding.

Field discovered that premature babies benefit greatly when they are massaged for 15 minutes, three times a day. After 10 days of massages, a premature baby will typically gain weight faster. In fact, the babies will gain weight 47 percent faster and leave the hospital six days earlier than those not massaged. On the average, the massaged preemies could also be expected to be more alert and active, have greater tolerance for noise, and sleep better. They also sleep more soundly and have fewer episodes of apnea.

A six-day early dismissal will save a hospital approximately $10,000 per baby. Considering there are about

425,000 premature births in America each year, the savings each year would amount to an incredible $4 billion!

The idea that touch and massage can heal is not new, but today's scientific research has confirmed it. Studies conducted by TRI and others have shown that a mere touch can improve our cardiovascular system by lowering blood pressure and reducing heart rate. This is why giving someone a simple hug can have such wonderful effects - for both the hugger and the huggee.

Massage and Your Immune System

Massage has also been shown to improve the immune function and reduce the levels of those two stress-causing hormones cortisol and norepinephrine. Two of the reasons you feel better after a massage is that it not only reduces the tension in your muscles, but it also stimulates the release of endorphins.

My wife, Christine, loves foot massages. After a long, tiring day as a day-care provider, she often comes home both physically and emotionally drained. When she can cajole me into giving her a foot massage, one of two things will happen. If it's early in the evening and she is not too tired, the foot massage will leave her alert and more energized. If she is tired and stressed out, a late-night massage will have a calming, soothing effect. After about 10 minutes, she is usually fast asleep. Yes, massage *is* medicine.

An interesting study was made of waitresses to determine how they could receive higher tips. Surprisingly, nothing the waitresses said or did influenced tips more than a simple touch. By simply placing her hand lightly on the shoulder of the person paying the bill, more often than not, the waitress received a higher tip.

Whether it's a child being held and hugged, lovers walking arm in arm, or an elderly person being embraced by a loved one, *all* will benefit, the huggers as well as those being hugged. In another TRI study reported in the August, '97 issue of *Life* magazine, volunteers over age 60 were first given three weeks of massage and then taught to administer massages to toddlers at a preschool.

Although the elderly volunteers benefitted from receiving massages, they benefitted **more** from giving the massages. After giving massages to the toddlers, "The seniors had lower levels of stress hormones, were less depressed and reported less loneliness. They had fewer doctor visits, drank less coffee and made more social phone calls." It's a funny thing about love - the more of it you give away, the more of it you receive.

It is more blessed to give than to receive.
                                        - Acts 20:35

There is more pleasure in loving than in being loved.
                                        - Thomas Fuller

...and in the end, the love you take is equal to the love you make.
                                        - Paul McCartney

✦✦✦✦✦✦✦✦

2

GOALS THAT SATISFY
THE HUNGRY HEART

The foolish person seeks happiness in the distance;
the wise man grows it under his feet.
                                        -James Oppenheim

Always continue the climb. It is possible for you to
do whatever you choose, if only you first get to know
who you are and are willing to work with a Power
that is greater than yourself to do it. If you want to
accomplish the goals of your life, you have to begin
with the spirit.
                                        - Oprah Winfrey

*W*hether your goal is to reduce stress, earn more money, become stronger spiritually or improve your health and overall performance, using affirmations on a regular basis can help you to realize your dreams. However, if you are not careful to balance your goals, they can conflict with one another. That is, striving toward one goal could undermine the realization of another.

For example, if one of your goals is to have a better relationship with your children and another goal is to work longer hours in order to increase your income, the attainment of one goal might well interfere with the realization of the other. Both of these goals demand time and energy; time you may not have and energy that you may simply run out of.

Some of the most pervasive and insidious problems people face arise because of the values that are promulgated by our culture. We are constantly being fed lies and false hopes. Do you really have to be brilliant and beautiful to feel good about yourself? Do you really have to be the "best" in order to be respected? Does wealth and an affluent lifestyle really define success and guarantee happiness? Is "*Look Out For Number One*" a good motto to live by?

> *No matter what you've done for yourself or for humanity, if you can't look back on having given love and attention to your own family, what have you really accomplished?*
>
> - Lee Iacocca

The Seductions of a Sick Society

If you fall for the seductions, false promises and warped

values of our society, you will experience added stress and frustration. If your goals are wrong, if they are motivated by greed and pride, how can their attainment - whether it's through positive thinking or any other means - bring the inner peace and joy that you seek? What good are riches if you can't sleep at night or if your kids are on drugs?

Today, many of us are worshiping at the feet of materialism. In the name of progress, money, comfort, and ease, we are blindly and happily skipping down the road that leads to disappointment. Our college students are attending schools that are being taught by materialists. When they get out, they will get a job and work for materialists. Our society tells us in a thousand ways that we can't be successful if we don't make a lot of money. Unfortunately, many have come to believe this myth.

Obviously, it is not money that is the problem. Becoming wealthy is not a sin. If we have money, we can do many wonderful things with it. It is the *love* of money, the obsession with it, that is the problem. It's the things people are willing to do to make the money. It is the parts of the soul that people are willing to sell over and over again to obtain it. In the name of money, all sense of balance goes out the window.

If your life is not balanced, what advantage is there in being a so-called high achiever, or a peak performer? In fact, the things you are doing to achieve your present goals may be contributing to your unhappiness. Before we can say "yes" to things that bring us true fulfillment, we must first learn to say "no" to those that cannot satisfy.

It is not enough to be busy...The question is: What are you busy about?
                                        - Henry David Thoreau

True Personal Development

Too many of us live our lives at a restless, frenetic pace; and what's worse, most of us are not even aware of it. We seem to be obsessed with having more and getting it now. This continues to be the "me, my, mine generation." Personal development is fine, but the obsessive drive for money and self-gratification can bring heartache rather than happiness.

Ironically, preoccupation with self can stifle our progress, while concern for others, and "loving our neighbors" can be of great benefit - not only to others but to ourselves. How can we experience personal development if it does not include lending a helping hand to those around us?

> *To have joy, one must share it. Happiness was born a twin.*
>
> - Lord Byron

There are those who have not sold out to the system, those who have discovered something fundamental. That authentic living and serenity can come only when we pay attention to the inner person as well as the outer person.

Most of us are fixated with the outer things; too few pay attention to the inner person and the spirit's need for nourishment. As you direct your focus and your actions toward that which cannot be seen: your motives, your purpose for living, your commitment to making this world a better place and your relationship to God, you will begin to experience the inner peace and joy that all people seek.

How to Satisfy the Hungry Heart

The obsession with money and material things will always increase the stress in life. Only goals that move us toward an integrated lifestyle are, in the final analysis, beneficial. Goals are integrated or harmonious if they assist all aspects of the person: mind, body and spirit.

As far as the body is concerned, we should all seek good health and high energy levels. As for the mind, who would deny that great knowledge and wisdom are wonderful attributes? But what good are these fine attributes of the body and mind if one does not have love?

As long as the attributes of the spirit, such as kindness, patience, forgiveness, and a thirst for the holy are not alive within the individual, that heart will remain "restless"; and the stress that attacks your mind and body will only increase.

God has made us for Himself, and the heart of man is restless until it finds its rest in Him. - St. Augustine

Noble Goals

One way to live a more integrated lifestyle is to establish goals that are noble. *Noble goals* are those that are stated in such a way that you absolutely must achieve them. They are totally within your power to complete. Secondly, they are goals that require and build character because they are connected to good values. A noble goal, when realized, will make you a stronger person and help you feel better about yourself. Goals that are noble concentrate on the means, or the process by which you achieve your goals, rather than the end result.

For example, let's assume you desire to try out for and make a college soccer team. Your noble goals would be to get the proper training, practice diligently, play soccer games as frequently as possible, maintain a positive attitude, and maintain this effort for as long as necessary.

Note that all of these goals and steps are actions that are within your power to achieve; virtually no one can stop you. If you act on these goals, you must succeed in completing them. If, instead, your goal is to actually make the team - something you are not in control of - there is a chance you will not succeed.

Making Your Dreams Come True

When you work toward a goal in this manner, you tend to concentrate on the excitement of the *now,* rather than the regrets of the past, or the fear of the future. When you are busy working on tasks that consume you, you bring yourself into the present moment. And it's easier to be at peace with yourself when you are concerned about today and all the wonderful things you can accomplish before you sleep.

> *Anxiety is nothing more than the avoidance of "now." If you live each moment as it comes, you can't be anxious or neurotic.*   - Dr. Wayne Dyer

In any endeavor, you are in charge of your own attitude and your own effort, but you are usually not in control of who is given the prize. This method of goal setting can be applied to every desire you have. If your outcome goal is to marry a particular person, you might write your noble goals in this way:

"I do all I can to develop a deep and loving relationship with Diane; I act with kindness, sensitivity, and integrity. I take care of my appearance, and I'm fun to be with. No matter what happens, I always stay true to who I am."

True, this man may never marry the woman of his dreams; his desire may not be fulfilled. However, all of his goals, as stated, can be achieved. Who's to stop him? And with their achievement would come a new-found sense of accomplishment. He will become a better human being. The only person this man would be competing against would be himself. His self-esteem would not decrease no matter what the end result. And the best part is that by working toward these goals, he has the best chance of achieving his ultimate goal - marrying Diane.

When I teach my students to select and write out their goals for the course, I no longer tell them to put all their energy and focus on the desired outcome - a grade of **A** for the course. I have seen students work extremely hard, do all the right things, and still not get a good grade. So instead, I teach them to write and strive for the following goals:

"I consistently come to class on time, pay close attention to the instruction, take good notes, do my home work every night and get extra help if I need it.

I learn to use relaxation techniques to stay calm and confident during exams. When I make mistakes, and have setbacks, I learn from them and carry on. I feel good knowing that I'm doing my best, regardless of what the final result may be."

Writing Noble Goals

Most of your goals can be written in this fashion. Using this method, the **steps** needed to accomplish one's ultimate desire become goals themselves. Noble goals *must* be reached because they are 100 percent attainable. When setbacks and negative outcomes occur, they are to be met with resilience and courage. When one possesses desire, discipline, persistence and a determination not to give up, success is certain. Students who set the goals described above, and read them frequently, usually obtain amazing results. Almost always, their grades go up significantly.

Take your current desires and try to convert them into goals that comply with this format. Goals written in this way offer profound advantages:

* The goals require attitudes and behaviors that are within your power to control; they are free from external competition.
* You are totally responsible for the outcome.
* Striving toward these goals requires strength of character and will also build character.
* The focus is placed on the **means**, or process, rather than the end result; since you know you can succeed,

this relieves you of unnecessary anxiety. (Fear of failing can impede your progress - worse, it can even prevent you from ever getting started.)
* By maintaining the right attitudes, and by completing your noble goals, you are in the absolute **best** position to have your ultimate desire fulfilled.
* Making mistakes and having setbacks are accepted as natural and normal. When you make a mistake, just say, "That's not like me, next time I'll do better."
* Even if the ultimate desire is not fulfilled, you can still say, "I have not failed, I have done my best, I have fought the good fight and been true to my values and ideals. I'm a better person because of this challenge, and the good habits I have learned will help me in the end."

The greater danger for most of us is not that our aim is too high and we miss it. But that it is too low and we reach it. - Michelangelo

For what will it profit a man, if he gains the whole world, but forfeits his soul? - Matthew 16:26

✦✦✦✦✦✦✦✦

3

FROM STRESS TO BLISS

Take time to laugh. It is the music of the soul. In life, pain is inevitable, but misery is optional.

Be not anxious for tomorrow, for tomorrow will take care of itself. Each day has enough trouble of its own.

- Matthew 6:34

I have been facilitating stress-management seminars for over ten years. In that time, I have studied and experimented with a number of stress-management techniques. Without doubt, one of the most popular and effective stress management techniques is the one developed by Harvard University Professor of Medicine Herbert Benson, M.D., and his team of researchers.

His study synthesizes recent scientific data with ancient religious beliefs and has resulted in a technique that has helped thousands to gain some control over the terrible psychological and physiological effects of the *fight-or-flight* response that we have come to know as stress.

In the late 1960's, Benson studied a group of volunteers who were practitioners of *Transcendental Meditation* or *TM*, a yoga form of meditation developed by Maharishi Mahesh Yogi. The TM technique is a surprisingly simple one. An instructor gives the practitioner a *mantra* - a special sound, word or phrase - that is supposed to be ideally suited to that person and is not to be disclosed to anyone.

The person is then taught how to assume a relaxed and passive attitude, breathe deeply, and concentrate on the mantra. If the mind begins to wander, the meditator simply brings his attention back to the mantra. The volunteers in the study meditated twice a day, for approximately 20 minutes each time while various measuring devices were attached to their bodies.

The research led to several remarkable conclusions. For starters, it was found that this meditative technique actually reversed all the negative effects brought on by the stress response - a response that causes an increase in blood pressure, rate of breathing, heart rate and the production of harmful hormones.

High blood pressure can lead to one of the most widespread and insidious health problems facing Americans today. Hypertension increases the rate of development of atherosclerosis, or hardening of the arteries, which can cause blocked blood vessels, which in turn, can lead to heart attacks and stroke.

The Focus Word

After observing the highly beneficial effects brought on

by the practice of TM, Benson theorized that if this form of meditation worked for people using a special mantra, perhaps another word or phrase could be substituted for the mantra with the same outstanding results.

You can imagine Benson's delight when his theory proved correct. He found that what was needed was not necessarily a designer-type mantra, but *any* focus word or mental device that would help shift the mind from logical, externally-oriented thoughts to a single point of interest; a thought which would serve to quiet the mind by keeping it focused.

Where Ancient Wisdom and Modern Science Meet

Benson's research led to the study of various ancient religious meditative techniques that appeared to elicit what he called the *Relaxation Response* - a state that is the very antithesis of the psychological and physical state that accompanies extreme negative stress.

In this relaxed state the systems of the body are repaired and rejuvenated. Since the person may be lying down with their eyes closed, he or she may seem to be asleep, but is actually awake; the brain wave patterns are distinctly different from those produced during sleep. Sleep cannot produce the specific health-promoting effects that the Relaxation Response does.

In his groundbreaking book, *The Relaxation Response*, Benson cites ancient writings and describes how a Christian meditator is advised to:

Sit down alone and in silence. Shut your eyes, breathe out gently and imagine yourself looking into your own heart. As you breathe out say "*Lord Jesus, have mercy on me.*" Say it, moving your lips gently or simply say it in your mind. Try to put all other thoughts aside. Be calm, be patient and enjoy the serenity that comes from silence.

An example of Jewish mysticism cited by Benson comes to us from the 13th century writings of Rabbi Abraham Abulafia. His meditative technique involved dwelling upon the names of God and the Hebrew letters that constitute those names. His system also stressed the importance of body posture and proper breathing.

Prepare to Relax

Benson and his Harvard team used their findings to develop a method for eliciting the Relaxation Response. The four essential components necessary to prepare for this technique include:

1. *A Quiet Environment* -
    A quiet place where you can sit or recline and be free of any outside distractions.

2. *A Focus Word* -
    A sound, word, or phrase to keep the mind from wandering or being distracted by outside thoughts.

3. *A Passive Attitude* -
    This is perhaps the most important factor in bringing about the Relaxation Response. Despite your best efforts, your mind will wander from your focus word; distracting thoughts will pop up now and then. When this happens do not be concerned or frustrated. Simply bring your mind back to your focus word and continue.

4. *A Comfortable Position -*
   The goal here is to avoid being distracted because of physical discomfort. Recline or sit and perform the muscle relaxation exercise. Breathe slowly, deeply and naturally from your stomach. Starting with the muscles in your feet, relax each muscle group in your entire body until your face and even your scalp are relaxed. When all your muscles are relaxed you are ready to meditate.

How to Evoke the Relaxation Response

Over the years I have found the following procedure to be an excellent way for most people to bring about the wonderful benefits of this exercise:

1. Sit or recline in a quiet, comfortable position and close your eyes.
2. Relax your muscles. Beginning with your feet, relax all the muscles in your body. Imagine a green light entering your body through your feet. Now visualize that healing light slowly moving upward through your body. Feel the deep relaxation as the light courses through your body and gently soothes each muscle group.
3. Once your muscles are relaxed (this should only take a few minutes) become aware of your breathing. Breathe deeply but naturally through your nose. Your stomach should rise slightly as you bring the air deep into your lungs. Then simply relax, or let go; the air will automatically leave your lungs. As you breathe

out, repeat your focus word silently to yourself. For example, if your focus word is, "relax," just breathe in, and as you exhale, quietly say, "relax."
4. Continue for 10 to 20 minutes.

Breathe deeply! It's the key to good health, affecting all sorts of body functions from the nervous system to circulation to digestion.
- Andrew Weil, M.D.

From Stress to Bliss

Most people who regularly evoke this response report a wide range of positive effects:

1. The most universal benefit is a release of muscle tension throughout the body. Many people experience relief from tension-induced backaches and headaches. Some people have learned to reduce, or even completely prevent the recurrence of migraines.
2. The heart rate slows down and blood pressure decreases.
3. Letting go of the concerns of the world for a few minutes each day often results in feelings of peacefulness, well-being and happiness. One will gain a greater ability to handle day-to-day challenges with calm and assurance.
4. Since your digestive system revs up, digestion improves.
5. The electrical activity in your brain changes from low

amplitude, rapid *beta waves* - which indicate external attention - to the slower, more peaceful, high amplitude *alpha waves*.

6. Because the body has rested, you feel rejuvenated and have more energy.

7. Since the stress response can take its toll on the immune system, this exercise can give it a boost. People who relax regularly are sick less often than those who don't.

8. Those who practice this exercise regularly increase their self-esteem and their acceptance of others.

9. Since relaxation allows a stronger flow of blood to the brain, it can allow easier access to the creative and problem-solving capacities of your brain.

10. Regular relaxation can result in an improvement in virtually any area that has been adversely affected by constant negative stress.

The Breath of Life

Notice the crucial role deep breathing plays in this exercise. One of the most important facts concerning good health is not widely known - ***The quality of your breathing is the most direct connection between your physical and emotional states***. By controlling your breathing you will gain greater control over your emotional well-being and you will do it quickly and naturally. Here are just some of the benefits of deep, relaxed breathing:

*   Your blood will be more fully cleansed and more oxygen will reach the cells throughout your entire body.

* The specialized cells of your immune system will be more effectively circulated to fight for your good health.
* The flow of your lymph fluid will be stimulated, aiding in the removal of waste and toxins from your body.
* You will have more energy and get rid of that fatigued or tired feeling.

Right now, wherever you are, take a deep relaxing breath; let the air fill your lungs so that your stomach bulges out. Hold it for two seconds, and exhale slowly and completely through your nose. Repeat this ten times. How do you feel? Get in the habit of doing this not only when you are feeling stressful, but whenever you want to relax or need a burst of energy. You can practice deep breathing anywhere and anytime: in the car, at work, at play, and while reading or watching TV.

Getting a Good Night's Sleep

Unlike strenuous exercise, following a strict diet, or intense study, practicing the relaxation exercise is not only good for you but it FEELS GREAT. Most people find that the best times to practice are either before breakfast or before dinner time.

This routine can also be used to help you to fall asleep at night. Whenever I have trouble falling asleep, instead of concentrating on my usual focus word, I simply concentrate on my breathing. That is, I imagine my stomach to be a balloon, expanding on the inhale and contracting on the exhale. As I continue to stay relaxed, breathe deeply and visualize my stomach rising and falling, I usually fall asleep within minutes.

There is no pillow as soft as a clear conscience.
                                        - Joshua Kahn

Beyond the Relaxation Response

After developing the relaxation response Benson discovered a way to improve the technique. He found that if one were to use a focus word or phrase that held some deep personal meaning, the benefits gained would be multiplied. He discovered that by using a religious or spiritual phrase which had special meaning to the practitioner, the peace, rest and rejuvenation came faster than if a neutral word were used.

Depending on your need, you might try any of the following phrases. Of course, it would be best to experiment with various phrases from your religious background until you discover what works best for you.

To Overcome:	**Use:**
Anxiety	* I cast my burdens upon the Lord.
	* The peace of God, which surpasses all understanding guards my heart and my mind.
Anger	* I am slow to anger, and quick to forgive.
	* The Lord gives me His strength, I am at peace with my fellow man.
Fear	* I fear no evil, for Thou art with me.
	* I can face all trials; my hand is enclosed within Yours.

Lack of Confidence	*	I can do all things through God who strengthens me.
Separation From God	*	As I walk toward God, He *runs* toward me.
	*	He said, "I will never leave you nor forsake you."
Resentment	*	As I forgive others, God forgives me.
	*	I forgive, and I am set free!
Worry	*	I am worry-free for God is with me.
	*	His mercy endures forever.
	*	Shalom.
Temptation	*	With each temptation, God supplies the means of escape.
Loneliness	*	God is near the broken-hearted.
	*	The Lord is my friend, He is always at my side.
Indecision	*	As I yield to God, He shows me the way.
	*	The Lord is a light unto my path.
Hopelessness	*	All will be fine for my hope is in the Lord.
	*	All things turn out for good for those who love the Lord.
Depression	*	I rejoice! This is the day the Lord hath made.
	*	Because I trust in You, I have perfect peace.
Sleeplessness	*	I sleep in *peace* - God has everything under control.
	*	Shalom.

Lovelessness	*	Love is patient, love is kind - *love never fails.*
	*	I love my neighbor as myself.
Defeat	*	God gives strength to the weary.
	*	The Lord sustains those who are fallen.
Low Self-Esteem	*	I *am* important - God loves me.

If you are currently suffering from excessive stress, turn to the section titled, ***Anxiety***, in **Part II**. Reflection on these verses will bring you the inner peace and strength needed to face the challenges of each new day.

The Most Powerful Predictor of Health and Longevity

A large number of recent studies, 193 in fact, have all come to the same surprising conclusion. The most powerful predictor of good health and long life is *not* diet, heredity, exercise, education or race - although all of these factors certainly do play a role - it is the degree to which your life is "stress-free."

Before continuing with an analysis of these studies, it is important to understand that it's almost impossible to be completely stress-free for long periods of time; nor should we want to be. Research has proven that we reach peak performance when we are experiencing a mild amount of stress. Whether you are taking a test, performing on stage, working on the job, competing in an athletic event, or simply involved in a conversation, a small degree of stress will help you to do a better job.

In the studies mentioned above, stress is defined as the extent to which you feel your life is out of your control. That is, being free of damaging negative stress is primarily determined by how much control you believe you have - whether it's within your home, at work, or in a classroom having to listen to a boring professor. Further, it is not the event itself that impacts us as much as it is your *perception* of the event. It is not what happens to you, but how you react to what happens to you.

One of the 193 studies was a follow-up of the classic study which began in the 1960s involving males employed by the British civil service. The data revealed that the higher the men's classification, the lower the rates of death.

In any culture, people at or near "the top" have greater control of their lives, or feel that they do. And those at or near the bottom usually lack control and experience much greater stress. Some of these studies tested this phenomenon among chimps and orangutans and the same results were found. On average, those at the top lived longer than those at the bottom of the social ladder.

Of course, stress is a relative thing. The head custodian in a large office building who gets along well with his staff and enjoys his work, would probably have less stress than the president of the company who does not get along with his "uncooperative and rebellious" subordinates, is dissatisfied with his relative position within the larger corporate world, and hates the unending competition of rival companies.

Sometimes, the stress we experience does not originate from the outside world, but from the neglect of our own inside world.

Soul Sickness

Often, the stress we experience in our lives is a result of what has been called *soul sickness* - the physical and psychological pain caused by a spirit that has not been properly nourished. When we neglect our spiritual health we should not be surprised when we suffer from things like stress, chronic guilt, confusion, paranoia, and their associated physical symptoms.

In her book, *Guilt is the Teacher, Love is the Answer*, author Joan Borysenko, Ph.D., writes of a fascinating encounter between Bill Wilson, one of the founders of A.A., and psychiatrist Dr. Carl Jung. In a letter written to Wilson, Jung tells him that alcoholism is too deeply seated to be cured by psychological means alone, and that Wilson's hopes lay in a "spiritual conversion." Ironically, Bill Wilson's life turned 180 degrees when he actually had that conversion, and out of it was born the 12-step programs. The fascinating story of Wilson's spiritual awakening and the incredible success of the Twelve-Step programs will be covered later in this book.

Although we are the ones who bring on most of our pain and suffering, sometimes our trials and troubles originate from another place - from a source you might not expect. In the next chapter, we'll take a look at that source.

The best doctors in the world are Dr. Diet,
Dr. Quiet and Dr. Merryman. - Jonathan Swift

You can't tell me that worry doesn't do any good.
The things I worry about don't happen!

✦✦✦✦✦✦✦✦

4

HOW SUFFERING BRINGS JOY

When one door of happiness closes, another opens;
but often we look so long at the closed door that we
fail to see the one which has opened for us.
                                        - Helen Keller

*W*hy do we suffer? Why must we go through trials and tribulations? Sometimes our troubles are the result of our own mistakes. Whenever we do something wrong or stupid there is always a price to pay (if not in this life, then in the life hereafter). We alone are responsible for our behavior and we cannot escape the consequences of our actions.

But not all of your suffering is your fault. There are times when it is *God* who allows trials and suffering to befall the ones He loves. However, He does it for a purpose. God wants to embrace us. He wants us to grow spiritually. When we are comfortable or blessed all the time, it is difficult for us to grow. We become too complacent.

It is when you have problems, disappointments, and moments of intense testing that you can say when you've come through it all, "I am stronger now because I've wrestled with and overcome this problem. I have learned something and from now on, my life will be different."

Why does God put us through the wringer? To fill us out. After we've been obedient to that which is right, He feeds us and fattens us up spiritually for the next time. And then He puts us through the wringer again - and again. And it's not going to stop until the day we die.

Why Good People Go Through Bad Times

Going through the wringer time after time is not a welcome prospect, but it is an exciting way of life. Although life is not fair, and trouble is inevitable, the feelings of satisfaction, self-esteem, and elation that follow a victory over a difficult problem or dilemma somehow compensate. Because you are important to Him, God works with you by working you over. He is your Father and as crazy as it sounds, He gives you joy and happiness by putting you through trials. Overcoming trials enables you to grow by becoming steadfast.

Steadfastness is firmness in purpose that can be gained only through knowledge and experience. Steadfastness is how you grow spiritually; it is the opposite of giving in to yourself and your self-serving tendencies. By remaining steadfast, you grow in character. God uses the person of strength and character to help repair the world.

Why Are You Tested?

It is important to understand that God sends testing and trials not so much to punish us, but "for the purpose of." He exposes us to trials and hardships in order to teach us something. He sends us difficult, challenging situations for a purpose. One reason is to help us to overcome a personal weakness.

If you have trouble getting along with people, God may place you in the close company of someone you can't stand so that you may learn the meaning of patience, tolerance and love. If you have trouble following orders, God may put you in a position where you are under the authority of someone you don't respect.

As you learn to deal with this person's authority, you will learn the meaning of humility. And ironically, once you learn humility and how to accept authority, you will have taken the first step toward becoming a strong leader.

The second reason God sends us trials is to bring us to a higher spiritual level. If you want to be used by God, you must be prepared for the challenges that lie ahead. He can only use those who have been tested by fire and have come out of the crucible wiser and better equipped to handle the work that has to be done. An example of this is found in the story of Job.

The Story of Job

The patience of Job is legendary and the torments through which God put that man are almost indescribable. Job was a righteous man and a prophet. He did everything he believed was right according to the knowledge he was given. But God allowed Satan, the Great Accuser, to test Job. In the story, Satan tells the Lord:

> *You have blessed the work of his hands, so that his*
> *flocks and herds are spread throughout the land. But*
> *stretch out your hand and strike everything he has*
> *and he will surely curse you to your face.*
>   -Job 1:10b-11

Job had been richly blessed by God. Satan was given permission by God to take away everything Job had - his sons, his daughters, and all of his wealth. He was left with nothing but terribly painful sores all over his body and a wife who told him to "curse God and die."

His three friends came to give the broken man "comfort" and "advice." They told Job, in essence, how terrible he was: "Everyone believed you were so righteous, but look at you. You're a mess. God is punishing you - confess your sins and repent, then God will forgive you."

What is the meaning of the story? What lessons are we to learn from it? Why would God do this to Job or anyone for that matter? The answer is, Job had to be taken to a new level. Yes, he was faithful and righteous. But Job was richly blessed by God; he was spiritually comfortable. It's easier to be happy and "good" when everything is going our way. What would Job do when those blessings were taken away? What would *you* do?

The Long Dark Night of the Soul

Although Job never denounced God, he began to complain and argue with Him. He became spiritually disoriented. God was hiding His face.

No doubt some of you have gone through a similar experience, one in which your faith was sorely tested. You call out to God, but He doesn't answer. He is there of course, but you can't feel His presence. The lines of communication are broken. As you cry out and beat your fists toward a cold and silent sky there is nothing but silence. All the crutches you normally rely upon are gone.

Eventually, you enter what has been called the *long dark night of the soul* - a period when you experience the depths of utter despair and helplessness. What are you to do? Let's continue our story and see how Job handled the problem.

Although Job was angry and confused he never denied God, *"Though He slay me, I will hope in Him. Nevertheless, I will argue my ways before Him."* (Job 13:15) Job asks God, "Why? Why are you doing this to me Lord?" But God never answers Job's question. God didn't and doesn't have to defend Himself, or explain Himself.

Instead, God emerges from an approaching whirlwind and approaches Job; He asks Job a series of questions:

> *Where were you when I laid the earth's foundation? Tell Me, if you understand. Who marked off its dimensions? Surely you know! Where are the foundations fastened? Or who laid the cornerstone, When the morning stars sang together, And all the sons of God shouted for joy?*   - Job 38:4-7

Job Sees the Light

Suddenly, Job saw the light. He came to understand that there are some things we will never know. There are some things we must simply accept. Through his ordeal, Job wrestled with God but never lost his faith. When he came to the realization that God is omnipotent and doesn't always explain Himself, Job had a change of heart and the terrible darkness began to lift. This story demonstrates another truth - **God will never let us suffer longer than is necessary for the lesson to be learned**. Once you learn that which you were intended to learn and change your actions accordingly, the darkness lifts and the trial ends.

Job had always been obedient, but obedience isn't all God wants from us. He wants *us*, the eternal you and the eternal me. He wants us to call upon Him and ask for His embrace, not just through physical blessings, but He wants us to want Him emotionally and spiritually, and to seek Him with all our hearts and to serve Him.

Before his suffering, Job knew of God. After his testing, Job knew God. He came into a personal relationship; he was brought to a new level of intimacy with God, *"I have heard of Thee by the hearing of the ear; But now my eye sees Thee."* - Job 42:5

Having allowed Job to go through this experience, the Lord saw that Job had changed and so, God blessed him:

And the Lord restored the fortunes of Job when he prayed for his friends, and the Lord increased all that Job had twofold ... And Job died, an old man and full of days.   - Job 42:10,17

The Advantages of Suffering

Being able to handle trials and trouble is extremely important. Suffering leads us to blessings that are greater than anything we have known previous to the suffering. God allows the troubles, the emptiness, and the feeling of hopelessness. These are gifts from the Almighty that allow us to build character.

If we persevere and do the right thing as we struggle through the trouble, we usually come to see that the trials were "blessings in disguise." Trials give us the opportunity to move toward His will (which is often difficult to discern).

God doesn't put you through a test so *God* can find out what you're made of. He already knows everything about you, even things you don't know about yourself. When the Lord tries and tests you, He is providing *you* with the opportunity to see who you really are and what you are made of. He tests us for our benefit, not His. Like looking in a mirror, we come face-to-face with our own character. And as the light of truth is cast upon the darkness within, we can begin to correct it.

Trials can make you stronger because the things you must do to survive require that you grow in some way. Just as a string is strongest at the place it was once broken and knotted, and a bone is strongest at the place it was broken and healed, so you will be strong in the area of your testing.

> *Consider it all joy, my brethren, when you encounter trials, knowing that the testing of your faith produces endurance. And let endurance have its perfect result, that you may be perfect and complete, lacking in nothing.*   *- James 1:2-4*

If you are in the midst of some great trial, if you are suffering physically or emotionally, read and reflect upon any of the biblical verses in **Part II**, under the titles, *Hope,*

Strength, Patience, Endurance, Victory Over Trials, and *When Trouble Comes.* You will find immeasurable help there.

Your Real Enemy

In the story of Job, Satan plays a crucial role. His actions and the actions of Job are there for our instruction. Satan acts only with divine permission, like a "lion on a leash." The Bible tells us that Satan is limited in what God will permit him to do. Satan tempts us by leading us into situations that appeal to our *yetzer ha-ra*, a Hebrew term meaning the evil impulse. Accordingly, he will hit you where you are weakest.

For some it might be lust or greed; for others it may be fear or pride. While Satan tempts us for the purpose of bringing us down, God allows us to be exposed to the dark side and tests us for the purpose of building us up. Yes, God's desire is for our personal development, not society's definition of personal development, but His. Satan wants you to fail. God wants you to succeed.

Knowing that we are subject to attack by insidious spiritual forces is important for several reasons. By acknowledging this enemy, we can begin to defend ourselves more effectively. A spiritual assault must be met on a spiritual battlefield - through good deeds, prayer, meditation and study.

Obviously, we are to do all we possibly can to help ourselves through our own efforts. This is why the traditional self-help tools and techniques have their value. But we are merely groping in the dark if we fail to enlist the aid of the One who can bring us victory on these invisible battle fronts.

Through faith, prayer, meditation, and noble living we gird ourselves with the invincible armor of the most high God. He may not remove your problem, but He will give you the courage and strength to walk through the troubled waters, not as a broken person, but as one who has hope and dignity. He may not change your outer circumstances, but cooperation with Him will change the inner *you*.

Mysteries We Can Never Solve

Sometimes it is impossible to know why God does the things He does. For example, we cannot know for certain why God would allow a baby to be born with a fatal disease or why He allows an entire population to die from widespread famine. I know this may sound wrong to many of you, but I believe there are some things we as humans may never know. At these times, we can only hold on to our faith and, like Job - who never got a direct answer to his questions - cry out: "I put my trust in Thee."

God doesn't love us because we are valuable; we are valuable because God loves us. He wants us to succeed and know the joy of being alive. He is not consumed with our weaknesses as we too often tend to be. He is consumed with our goodness and our potential.

Every life has plenty of rubbish, a lot of junk in it, but among the ashes, the wood, the hay and the stubble that will be burned in judgment, there are precious stones, jewels and gold. God comes to burn the wood, hay, and stubble and gather the precious things that He finds among them.

Your joy is your sorrow unmasked. And the self-same well from which your laughter rises was often times filled with your tears. - *Kahlil Gibran*

✦✦✦✦✦✦✦✦

5

FINDING YOUR PURPOSE FOR LIVING

Many persons have a wrong idea of what constitutes true happiness. It is not attained through self-gratification but through fidelity to a worthy purpose.   *- Helen Keller*

$\mathcal{W}$e are all looking for something; something which will help make us happier and more fulfilled. Everyone has a specific purpose in life, and if you discover what it is, you will come closer to the happiness and fulfillment you seek. The need for meaning is not a physical need like the need for food or water. It is not a psychological need for self-esteem or recognition. Finding meaning and purpose is a spiritual need; it is a thirst of the soul.

We are all here to fulfill a mission. And God has given each of us unique talents and abilities to fulfill that mission. You have been given the ability to do something better than anyone else in the world. When you match your unique and special talent with some human need, you will experience an excitement, an energy and a joy that will seem boundless.

What is the perfect task for *your* life? You don't know. How do you go about finding it? According to the prophets you will find it as you seek and follow God's will and dive into the recesses of your own heart in order to discover who you really are. In the process you will make a thousand mistakes and you will fall more times than you can imagine.

But as you act, fall and get up again - time after time - one morning you will wake up and you will know. And like a tiny spark that grows into a great fire which cannot be put out, that idea will grow in your mind. One of the keys to finding your purpose is to know what motivates you.

The Theory of Motivation

American psychologist Abraham Maslow developed what he called the *hierarchical theory of motivation*. He believed human behavior could be explained by our desire to reach certain goals, the realization of which would make our lives rewarding and meaningful. As soon as one personal goal is reached, another arises to take its place. Consequently, complete satisfaction can only be temporary. Behavior is explained, therefore, in terms of motivation; we are always in a state of wanting to achieve the next goal.

Maslow theorized that not only are personal goals ingrained, but they are arranged in an ascending hierarchy of priority, or levels. As one level or set of personal goals is sufficiently satisfied, the next higher set of desires emerges and becomes the dominant motivator in our lives.

Maslow's Need-Hierarchy of Human Motivation

Level	Needs
1 -	Physiological
2 -	Safety and security
3 -	Belongingness and love
4 -	Self-esteem
5 -	Self-actualization

For example, if you were dying of thirst or starvation, your main motivation would be food and water. You would think of little else until this *Level 1* set of needs was satisfied. Once these needs were substantially met, you would become aware of and be motivated by the second level of needs.

All or most of your physiological/survival needs would have to be adequately satisfied before you would turn to the next level - safety and security. Once the needs in the second level were adequately satisfied, their motivating force would diminish, and you would begin to be concerned with and motivated by belongingness and love etc. A description of each *needs level* follows:

* *Physiological* - Oxygen, food, water, sex, shelter.

* *Safety and Security* - Includes an adequate degree of order and predictability in one's immediate environment. This is

especially important for infants and children who need to know they are safe.

* ***Belongingness and Love*** - Kind, loving relationships; inclusion in a warm, caring family or group. Satisfaction of these needs will stave off feelings of loneliness, rejection and alienation. We all have a need to feel liked and respected.

* ***Self-Esteem*** - Our feelings of self-worth and self respect.

* ***Self-Actualization*** - To desire to become, or *actualize,* all that one feels he or she is capable of becoming; to accomplish - to a substantial degree - all that one senses he or she *can* accomplish. The need to be making progress toward a personal goal. The self-actualized person has turned perceived potential into reality.

As the lower, more basic needs are satisfied, the higher-level needs become the dominant motivational force in a person's behavior. Of course, there are exceptions to this need level formula. But generally speaking, this list can serve as a guide to what would "normally" motivate people. Understanding this motivational needs process puts you in a better position to find your purpose in life.

Finding Your Purpose in Life

There are two steps to follow which will help you to find your purpose and become a "self-actualized" person:

1. Identify those activities where you do better than most people; the things which come easily to you; that

which you do exceedingly well; the areas where you excel.

2. Identify the things you enjoy doing. What activities give you pleasure and satisfaction?

After you have answered the questions above, you should have found one or two areas where you might pursue your passion. If that which you identify is consistent with God's will (which you may come to know if you stay close to Him and His word), you might very well have found your purpose. When you find a task, career or mission which combines your talents with the things you love to do, and if that task somehow makes the world a better place - then you have found your life's mission.

The Power of Love

Gerald Jampolsky, M.D., psychiatrist and author of the book, *Love is Letting Go of Fear*, tells of a fascinating documentary he saw which illustrated the incredible power of love and finding one's purpose in life. The documentary is about Father Watson, a priest who lived in the southwestern part of the United States. He was about 50 years of age and had been a relatively healthy man all of his life.

He developed stomach trouble and went to a physician where it was discovered that not only did he have cancer of the stomach, he had cancer in almost every organ in his body. He was told that neither chemotherapy nor surgery would be effective. Since he had only a few months to live, his doctor advised him to get his affairs in order.

Father Watson decided to go to Mexico City to visit a

small church. One day a little boy came in and stole the "poor box," where money was deposited for the members of the congregation who were destitute. The priest ran after the boy, caught him and found out that the boy was an orphan who had been physically beaten and sexually abused. Although Father Watson did not have long to live, he decided to adopt the little boy.

This documentary was about Father Watson and his 5,000 orphans - *25 years later!*

Since the mind, body and spirit are all connected, the health of one affects the health and strength of the other two. Finding and living your purpose will help you to know joy and inner peace. It will energize you and add years to your life. If you work hard at it you will one day find your reason for living. You will know when you have found your purpose, because you will have almost limitless energy. And when you find it, it will burn like a "fire in your belly."

When love and skill work together, expect a masterpiece.
                                        - John Ruskin

The great thing in this world is not so much where we are, but in what direction we are moving.
                                        - Oliver Wendell Holmes

✦✦✦✦✦✦✦✦

6

THE HAPPIEST PEOPLE
IN THE WORLD

*And if you give yourself to the hungry, and satisfy the
desire of the afflicted, then your light will rise in the
darkness, and your gloom will become like midday.*
- Isaiah 58:10

eople who volunteer to help others, describe what
has become known as the *healthy helping syndrome,* a term
coined by Allan Leks and Peggy Payne - coauthors of the
book, *The Healing Power of Doing Good.* According to their
studies, this syndrome has two phases.

The first phase is **physical** in nature. In this phase,
volunteers report an upsurge of energy and a decrease or
absence of pain and fatigue. It appears that *endorphins* - those
natural brain chemicals that reduce pain and help create a feel-

good sensation - have much to do with this helping syndrome. Studies have shown that when one is engaged in volunteer work, endorphins are produced, resulting in a substantial increase in energy, drive and good health.

How to Be Happy

The second phase of this helping syndrome is **emotional** in nature. People who volunteer feel better about themselves; they enjoy a long lasting improvement in their emotional state in several ways. Volunteers report a heightened sense of self-worth, greater happiness, optimism, and a decrease in feelings of helplessness and depression. Want to overcome stress and depression? Here's a great way for people to raise their self-esteem.

These positive emotions typically last a relatively long time. Whereas the initial energy boost that takes place in the first phase may only last for several hours, the sensation of inner satisfaction and well-being that occurs in the second phase can last for days.

A Gallup survey comparing people who exercise regularly with those who volunteer found that although a healthy 44 percent of those who exercise regularly reported "gains in self-worth," a whopping 57 percent of the volunteers in the survey reported a gain in this area.

Can you imagine what your involvement in both activities - aerobic exercise *and* volunteering - would do for your physical, emotional and spiritual well-being? From all indications, doing for others is one of the best ways to reduce stress and increase your zest for life. So, what are you waiting for?

The Mother Teresa Effect

Leks conducted a national survey of volunteers. He discovered that 95 percent of respondents claimed they experienced the helper's high. Of this group, nine out of ten rated their overall health as significantly better than others in their age group. This improvement began when they started volunteering. The frequency of service was also relevant. The people who reportedly received the highest benefits were those who helped out once a week.

Some have come to call these physical and emotional changes that take place within the volunteer, the *Mother Teresa effect*. Many believe that this helping syndrome is what helped empower Mother Teresa, founder of the *Missionaries of Charity*, to work as long and as hard as she did. Despite her advanced age and small stature, Mother Teresa worked with such strength and endurance that it astounded all those around her.

Although she was constantly surrounded by death and disease, this woman of valor remained relatively healthy for most of her life. With virtually limitless energy and drive, Mother Teresa accomplished what can only be described as miracles, as she first rescued, and then brought comfort to the poorest of the poor in India and other parts of the world.

God does not command that we do great things, only little things with great love.

- Mother Teresa

Give and You Will Receive

According to the research data, the benefits obtained by those who helped others were greatest if they:

Made personal contact
Person-to-person contact with the people being helped is more beneficial to the helper, than when there is little or no contact.

* *Met face-to-face on a regular basis*
The survey respondents who had personal contact with those being helped reported the highest (95 percent) health-enhancing benefits. Of this group, those who served from two to four hours on a weekly basis seemed to benefit most.

* *Exerted effort*
The ones who exerted some degree of physical or mental energy were the ones who were most energized. It is when we are out there working to comfort people in their hour of need or helping them to help themselves that we empower ourselves.

* *Focused on the process rather than the results*
Our actions are most efficacious when we concentrate on what we must do now - at this moment, on this day. When we are overly concerned with the final results - in this case, with whether or not our efforts are really helping the other person - we can suffer from frustration and a sense of futility whenever steady "progress" is not being made.

The happiest people in the world are those who have learned the power of love.

Hatred paralyzes life; love releases it. Hatred confuses life; love harmonizes it. Hatred darkens life; love illumines it.
                              - Dr. Martin Luther King Jr.

You Are What You Do

In the Book of *James*, in the New Testament, we find:

What good is it my brother, if a man claims to have faith but has no deeds? Can such faith save him?
                              - James 2:14

Yea, a man may say, thou hast faith, and I have works: show me your faith without works, and I will show you my faith by my works.   - James 2:18

For as the body without the spirit is dead, so faith without works is dead also.   - James 2:26

This teaching, which is common to virtually all religions, is crystal clear. Faith must become an act, and faith that does not become an act is not faith; but merely a statement of what you believe. What you believe in your head is not going to do anything for anybody. If you believe that honesty, justice and mercy are good, but fail to put these beliefs into action - you're nothing but a hypocrite who says he has faith.

The spirituality of a person is determined by the experience of the person. You are not spiritual because of your beliefs. You are not spiritual because of your interests. You are spiritual because of what you do. Good actions emanating from a pure heart define spirituality. In essence, you are what you do, and you do what you are.

Happiness is an Attitude

People are just about as happy as they make up their minds to be.   - Abraham Lincoln

Honest Abe was right - being happy is an attitude. And attitudes are something we can control. Happiness depends more on your *response* to what actually happens to you than what happens to you. Most people believe that negative events must elicit negative reactions. This is not true. Problems do not have to make you unhappy. Happiness or sadness is almost always a personal choice.

So don't wait for that perfect mate, the big beautiful home, the excellent job, perfect health or anything else before you decide to be happy. There's no need to wait. It's almost impossible to be unhappy when you have the right attitude, and having the right attitude has much to do with being appreciative of what you already have.

People who tend to be happy understand a basic truth. This truth enables them to remain hopeful when others want to give up. Smile when others can't help weeping. Fly with the wings of the wind when others can only crawl. This basic truth is for all who would claim it for their own - it's free. It is a heart filled with the attitude of *gratitude*.

When you face your Maker, you will have to account for all those God-given pleasures of life which you failed to enjoy.
                                        - The Talmud

Happiness depends to some extent upon external conditions, but chiefly upon mental attitudes. In order to be happy one should have good health, a well-balanced mind, a prosperous life, the right work, a thankful heart, and, above all, wisdom or knowledge of God.
                            - Paramahansa Yogananda

Find a need and fill it, find a hurt and heal it.
                            - Dr. Robert Schuller

✦✦✦✦✦✦✦✦

7

THE SADDEST PEOPLE IN THE WORLD

In the west we have freedom, but freedom has been perverted into license - a freedom toward evil. Man's sense of responsibility to God and society has grown dimmer and dimmer.

- Alexander Solzhenitsyn

The American culture is in a terrible state of decline. And because our culture strongly influences the way we think and behave, these troubling elements can present serious roadblocks to our quest for a rewarding and fulfilling life.

New ways of thinking and behaving that are personally and socially destructive have seeped into the American psyche. We can see it in our values, schools, pop music and entertainment, in our politics and in our voracious appetite for instant self-gratification.

Empowered living - being all you can be in your body, mind and spirit - is harder to attain when you are not aware of the ways our culture can either help or hinder your progress. Some of the enticements within our culture can become virtual land mines to personal fulfillment. Your pursuit of personal excellence will be greatly facilitated by an understanding of our society's failings and the obstacles they present to your happiness.

Compared to earlier generations, contemporary Americans are affluent, and this affluence has helped create an unprecedented amount of idle time and boredom. In his book, *Slouching Toward Gomorrah,* Robert H. Bork warns, "Bored, affluent people in a society that no longer possesses the disciplinary tools of shame and stigma will indulge the most primitive human emotions." In such an environment, promiscuity, violence, and substance abuse tend to grow to epidemic proportions - and they have.

Today's enormous technological advances have given us an increase in free time and an unprecedented opportunity to gratify our desires. When an insatiable thirst for pleasure meets the opportunity to satisfy all of those pleasures, we have a recipe for disaster.

Secular Madness

Our society is predominantly secular in nature. *Secularism*, which means without God, promotes the belief that morality is not dependent upon spiritual considerations - that there are no absolute and universal truths that are eternal and unchanging. Secularism implies that morals and values are relative. To the average well-educated American, belief in God is seen as unimportant, and to some, dangerous. Religion is often met with ridicule and disdain by the *cultural elite* - the people and institutions that define or shape our culture - for example, educators, the media, the entertainment industry and authors.

As you travel the path to excellence and inner fulfillment, you should understand the pernicious role this secular world-view can play in your life. If you denigrate or ignore your spiritual essence, the most important part of your being will weaken. When the soul is neglected, a sense of emptiness and meaninglessness will surely follow. You will not feel "complete." Your successes ultimately come to feel hollow for they can not satisfy the inner longings of a heart that senses that something is missing.

People who neglect the hunger of the soul are the saddest people in the world.

Whereas religion assumes the answers to life lie with God and His prescriptions for living nobly, the secularist assumes solutions to all personal and social problems lie within man himself. To the secular humanist, man is seen as "basically good" and, given the proper upbringing and education, capable of fixing all of society's ills. Help from God is neither possible nor necessary.

The Judeo-Christian view of humankind is not nearly as sanguine. In this view, human nature is basically flawed - humans have an innate propensity to live selfishly and do evil. We are incapable of solving the world's problems without divine assistance. Although we have the *potential* to live righteously, we must seek help and guidance from the Creator. We can't do it on our own. Evil comes naturally, while goodness must be learned, nurtured and practiced until it becomes habit. Instead of living independent of God, the spiritual person cooperates with Him.

If we live every moment of our lives in the secular world, we will come to define success and happiness in secular terms. The world will be a battlefield, a constant struggle for advancement and advantage, dividing us into winners and losers.

- Harold Kushner

Our Human Nature

It is difficult to pinpoint the beginnings of our current secularist world-view, but some of the philosophical foundations were first laid during the late seventeenth and early eighteenth centuries during the *Enlightenment.* This period was characterized by a renewed faith in human nature and in the power of reason to solve all of society's problems. Man came to be seen as basically good, who would, under the right environmental conditions, naturally behave nobly.

Under this philosophy, people who are not contaminated by a rotten home environment or a corrupt culture would naturally mature into people of virtue and contribute to the betterment of their society. If left in a natural state, unencumbered by the evils of a corrupt society, children would grow to become, according to French philosopher Jean Jacques Rousseau, "noble savages."

During the Enlightenment, Rousseau became the high priest of this romantic notion of innate goodness. All people, he declared, are born fountains of virtue and pearls in progress, and if left free to develop in a loving, nurturing environment, would become caring, magnanimous and productive.

Unfortunately, this naive but popular theory has had a devastating impact in the area of modern American education.

Chaos in the Classrooms

In 1940, school teachers were asked to list what they felt were the greatest threats to the educational process. In 1990, a similar list was requested. Note the differences in the two lists.

	1940	**1990**
First-	Talking out of turn	Drug abuse
Second-	Chewing gum	Alcohol abuse
Third-	Making noise	Pregnancy
Fourth-	Running in the halls	Suicide
Fifth-	Getting out of line	Rape
Sixth-	Wearing improper clothing	Robbery
Seventh-	Being wasteful with paper	Assault

(Source- *US News and World Report*)

By adopting the secular humanist approach to education, many of our schools are contributing to the problems that are besieging them. According to this philosophy, since people are basically good, the main responsibility of our schools is to provide a supportive and accepting environment - one that psychologist Carl Rogers calls *unconditional positive regard*.

Such an environment will permit that inner seed of goodness to blossom.

Consequently, most schools no longer seek to inculcate good values or strengthen students' characters. Instead, our youth are being asked to define and "clarify" their own values without judging them. This has become known as *values clarification.*

Values are no longer classified as right or wrong, good or evil; they are viewed as neutral. Generally, all opinions and ideas are to be equally respected as long as they can be defended. A *value* is seen as that which you enjoy doing. In this environment, there are no absolutes; everything is relative. If it seems right to you and you can "defend" it, that value is right for you. The popular saying by pop psychologist Fritz Perls romanticized this philosophy and became a sixties mantra:

> *You do your thing, and I'll do mine, and if by chance we meet, that is beautiful.*

It sounds good, doesn't it? But can you imagine a society living by such a totally self-gratifying and asinine creed? Unfortunately, many in our society are doing just that. There are many, for example, who are just "doing their thing" by having children out of wedlock. Most of these children end up in single-parent homes when one of the parents (usually the father) decides to leave the home and go into the world to do more of his "own thing."

Children who do not have sufficient access to one or both parents suffer a terrible price in emotional security and self-esteem. Unbelievably, more than one study has found that even when fathers are present in the home, "on average, they spend less than 30 seconds per week in meaningful conversation with their children."

Children of single parent homes are part of some very disturbing statistics:

* 95% of all prisoners.
* 85% of juveniles in state correctional institutions.
* 73% of all teen pregnancies.
* 64% of all teen suicides come from single parent households.

The Mis-Education of Our Youth

Years ago, as my wife Christine and I were driving our twin sons, Jesse and Gabriel, to Binghamton University in up-state New York to begin their college education, I explained that while they were away at school, they would encounter many temptations. And there was one in particular that would be more dangerous than any of the others. I explained how our nation in general, and our colleges and universities in particular, are predisposed to treat faith in God and spiritual matters as silly and irrelevant.

By the time our sons graduated and returned home four years later, they had come to believe that God and spiritual matters "were not important." Our worst fears were realized. As a professor, I can tell you that this sentiment is not uncommon among the average college student. I often hear students saying, "religion is for weak people who need an emotional crutch," or words to that effect.

I am happy to report that since their return home, Gabriel and Jesse have reaffirmed their faith and commitment to God and His word. Their decision has been accompanied by a dramatic transformation in several areas of their lives. They have become more loving and considerate toward their parents and others. They now go out of their way to help other people, and are also happier and more at peace with themselves.

The Breakdown of Morality

Recently, the Cable News Network presented the results of an interesting nation-wide survey. When Americans were asked: *What is the greatest threat facing America today?* the responses were as follows:

* 48% - A decline in morality
* 28% - A failing economy
* 24% - A foreign military threat or terrorist attack

Years ago, people were not as concerned about social deviance or the absence of family values as they are today. In the last three decades we have - to use a phrase coined by New York Senator Daniel Patrick Moynihan - "defined deviancy down." What was once considered deviant no longer is. We are not shocked when two people are murdered in a drive-by shooting. Perhaps, if 12 people were gunned down during a drive-by we would sit up and take notice, but I'm not so sure. In the *American Educator*, journalist Gertrude Himmelfarb reported, "The St. Valentine's Day Massacre in Chicago in 1929, when four gangsters killed seven other gangsters, shocked the nation and became legendary, immortalized in encyclopedias and history books. In Los Angeles today, as many people are killed in a single weekend." That which used to shock or terrify us has become commonplace. We have become accustomed to acts that once horrified us. We are experiencing atrocity overload. People who are too young to remember "how it used to be" are at an even greater disadvantage than the rest of us. To them, these things seem normal.

According to a report issued by the *Index of Leading Cultural Indicators*, since 1960 we have seen:

* Violent crimes triple (from 1,900 per 100,000 people in 1960 to 5,700 by 1992).
* Illegitimate births triple.
* Divorce rates increase by 400 percent.
* Single-parent families increase by almost 300 percent.
* The prison population increase by 600 percent. (The United States has more people in prison than any other country in the world.)

These exploding rates of social pathologies are all signs of a civilization falling apart. They are signs of social devolution, not evolution. Despite our nation's blessings in the areas of material goods, leisure time, political liberty, social mobility, and racial and sexual equality, we are paying a heavy price for a society gone rotten. We are in the midst of the greatest threat to the traditional American family this nation has ever faced.

We have known about the correlation between illegitimate births and crime for some time. Communities with a large percentage of single parents (which includes divorced couples), have dramatically higher rates of unemployment, crime, school dropouts, and drug and alcohol addiction. On the other hand, the popular belief that poverty or unemployment causes crime is a myth.

The Great Depression

You may be surprised to learn that the Great Depression of the 1930s was marked not only by wide-spread poverty, but by a relatively *high* degree of morality and *low* crime rates. In the high unemployment years of 1949, 1958, and 1961, when unemployment was 6 or 7 percent, crime was less than 2 percent. In England, in the 1890s, in a period of severe unemployment, crime actually fell.

Difficult times do *not* cause social deviance. The choice to do either right or wrong is always yours. Responsibility and accountability for the path you choose, no matter how "unfair" life has been to you, and no matter how unbearable your present circumstances, are yours and yours alone.

The weaker religion is in a society, the stronger its prisons had better be.

- Dennis Prager

The Hedonist

We are fast becoming a *hedonistic* society. In such a society, anything that makes you comfortable, anything that makes you warm, anything that makes you grateful and happy, anything that keeps your spirits up - whether it's taking a mood-altering drug, avoiding meaningful work, or having an illicit sexual affair - is seen as good.

But anything that upsets you, depresses you, is inconvenient, or isn't what you like - whether it's being responsible, doing homework, or visiting a sick relative - is seen as unpleasant and therefore, bad. This thinking can become a philosophy and a way of life. Things that make you unhappy or uncomfortable are avoided at all costs. The hedonist is self-indulgent and is obsessed with his feelings; his motto is: *"If it feels good, do it!"*

Unbridled self-gratification is fast becoming the norm. The hedonists are incredibly self-centered and demand to be unhindered in their pursuit of pleasure. In their endless quest for fun and excitement, hedonists fail to understand that in some ways, life is like a symphony. Music which consists of nothing but high notes is nothing but noise. It takes the highs and lows, as well as silence and sound to make a beautiful symphony - and a beautiful life.

The perpetual search for comfort and amusement, coupled with the wonders of modern technology have made it easier to be lazy and unproductive. Television, video games, and computers have made it possible for us to squander precious time in a sea of vulgarity and emptiness. Our nation's attraction for salacious TV productions and pornographic computer websites are testimonies to our descent into the gutter.

The Great Lie of the Feminist Movement

There is much within the feminist movement that is praiseworthy. Because of it, women have made tremendous gains in many key areas of life. But there is one aspect of *radical* feminism that has deceived and hurt millions of women. It is the false and destructive notion that women who decide to stay home to nurture and train their young children rather than go to work are making a terrible mistake because they are robbing themselves of personal fulfillment.

The most pernicious aspect of the radical feminist movement is that it ridicules and demeans all women who decide to stay home and work at being a mother and a homemaker. This myth is supported and perpetuated by large segments of the cultural elite and has contributed to the weakening of the family structure and created a multitude of personal and social crises. When women come to agree with this lie yet inwardly feel opposing emotions, they often experience guilt and depression.

As Maggie Gallagher has so accurately pointed out in her book, *Enemies of Eros: How the Sexual Revolution Is Killing Family, Marriage, and Sex and What We Can Do About It*, "Liberal feminism triumphed by telling a lie about nearly all women - and men. The work women do in families may not perhaps, seem great compared to inventing a new morality, or discovering the cure for cancer. But it compares quite favorably, in value, meaning, and social productiveness with being a vice-president for public affairs of General Motors, say, or a partner in an advertising firm. And it is necessary that we start saying so."

The Most Important Job on Earth

Certainly, the reality of today's economy often necessitates two incomes. Some mothers find that at some point, they have no choice but to go to work. But others go to work because they simply refuse to fight a culture that tells them in a thousand ways that a career and an extra paycheck are more important than nourishing a human soul. The same culture that tells them that by "getting out of the house" they can make more money, improve their self-esteem, and have fun doing it.

Many women have erroneously come to believe that they can "have it all" - be a loving, caring, effective mom and still have a demanding, full-time job while their new-born infants are in child care. They have swallowed the lie that "quality" time can make up for a lack of "quantity" time. While an added income will no doubt contribute to a higher standard of living, the price that must be paid is often too high.

What good is a new car, nice vacations, and more expensive clothing if parents are stressed out, unhappy, and too tired to communicate with their children? What's the advantage of being a working mom if her unsupervised teenage children are more likely to be disrespectful, failing in school, and in trouble with the law?

Imagine the joy and satisfaction a married couple will experience when they see their young children grow to become decent, well-adjusted individuals making contributions to society. What greater purpose can we, as parents, have than to be available to nurture, guide, and discipline our children so that they grow to become good, solid parents themselves?

Having a career in those early formative years does not guarantee that one's children will have serious problems, but statistics show that it does increase the chances. Similarly, working at home during a child's early years does not insure the inner growth and prosperity of your child - but on the average, it does make it more likely.

In the World, But Not of It

Since we have to live in the world as it is, we should learn all we can about it. However, it's another thing to be involved with it emotionally and personally; not just getting your feet wet, but getting in up to your rear-end or over your head is no way to advance spiritually. Being totally immersed in the values of this world - being *of* it - is worldliness.

It is delusional to believe that you can be of this world and still be aligned with your spirit. If you persist in being the hedonist - the self-indulgent person who follows the pattern, the social banter, the thinking and the immoral philosophy of this world - then your soul cannot grow to greatness.

The Greatest Obstacle to Personal Development

How, in the midst of this spiritual wasteland, can we hope to advance spiritually? One who would experience fulfillment is one whose heart and mind are made right, but your heart and mind cannot be right - no matter how intelligent you are - if you are proud. And if you believe you are humble and are proud of it, then you do not have humility.

All sinful thoughts and actions emanate from the same place - personal pride. **Pride is the most evil thing about us**. Most of us are unaware of how insidious pride is. We are unaware of the things we do because of pride, and the positive things we fail to do because of it. Your pride will prevent you from doing what is right and will also cause you to do what is wrong.

When there is sin in your life that you just cannot seem to stop, know that help does exist! Reading the Bible verses in

Part II under the heading, *Pride*, for example, will help you to overcome this, and many other character flaws. As humans, we may have a propensity toward sin, but it need not determine our destiny. We *can* rise above our natural tendencies and become the sons and daughters of a better world.

> *The intent of man's heart is evil from his youth.*
> - Genesis 8:21b

The Greatest Commandment

Christians, Jews and Muslims profess faith in the same Father God - the God of Abraham, Isaac, and Jacob. When Moses received the Ten Commandments on Mount Sinai, he was instructed by God to teach the people laws and principles by which to guide their lives. Two of those commandments have become embodied within the holiest prayer and declaration of faith in all Judaism. It is known as *The Shema* (shema means "hear," or "listen"). The first two lines of this prayer are:

> *Hear, O Israel! The Lord is our God the Lord is One! And you shall love the Lord your God with all your heart, with all your soul, and with all your might.*
>
> *- Deuteronomy 6:4-5*

In the book of Leviticus, we read how God instructed Moses to teach the people another command: *"You shall love your neighbor as yourself."*- Leviticus 19:18b

People are often amazed to discover how many of Jesus' teachings come directly from the Old Testament. Compare the verses above with those from the book of Matthew where we read:

And one of them, a lawyer, asked him a question, testing him. "Teacher, which is the greatest commandment in the Law?" And he said to him, "You shall love the Lord your God with all your heart, and with all your soul, and with all your mind. This is the great and foremost commandment. And a second is like it, You shall love your neighbor as yourself. On these two depend the whole Law and the Prophets.   — Matthew 22:35-40

Note the importance placed on loving your neighbor *as yourself.* Having a healthy regard for yourself is crucial - we might even say a prerequisite - to being happy. It's difficult to love others when we don't like who we are. In the next chapter we are going to learn how to like ourselves in a deeper, more unshakable way and, at the same time, take a look at the many myths that surround this idea of self-esteem.

The real crisis of our time is spiritual. If we have full employment, greater economic growth, more possessions, a higher standard of living, but our children have not learned to walk in goodness and justice and mercy, then the American experiment no matter how gilded, will have failed.
                — Dr. William Bennett

✦✦✦✦✦✦✦✦

8

The Surprising Truth About Self-Esteem

No man who is occupied in doing a very difficult thing, and doing it very well, ever loses his self-respect.

- George Bernard Shaw

In the last decade, more has been written in this country on the subject of self-esteem than virtually any other subject. More than 10,000 scientific studies of self-esteem have been conducted. No one would deny that as a general prescription for child-rearing, fostering self-esteem is beneficial. All children need and deserve a loving parent or guardian who provides a safe and supportive environment.

Healthy self-esteem is a good thing but unfortunately, there are many myths surrounding it.

Many see the self-esteem movement as the great national panacea that will solve all of our social problems. In 1983, California set up a task force to promote self-esteem. They argued that a "lack of self-esteem is central to most personal and social ills plaguing our state and nation." They saw self-esteem as a kind of national elixir, "a social vaccine that enables people to live responsibly and that inoculates us against the lures of crime, violence, substance abuse, teen pregnancy, child abuse, chronic welfare dependency and educational failure." (California Task force, 1999, *Toward a State of Self-esteem*)

The Theory

Increase your self-esteem, their theory goes, and your confidence and attitude will improve. You will naturally accomplish more and become a better person. By learning to love and accept yourself just the way you are, you will become a good person. If you feel good about yourself, you will do the right thing and succeed at virtually everything you attempt. An interesting theory.

For more than fifteen years, an increasing number of elementary school administrators and educators across the land have sought to convince children that they are "wonderful and special people." Using this self-esteem approach, students habitually receive profuse praise and admiration even when the praise is inappropriate or undeserved: "Oh look, you spelled your name correctly and even dotted your I's, how wonderful!"

Self-esteem is widely believed to be the key to personal

development and excellence. Parents and educators have been encouraged to do whatever possible to help raise their charges' self-esteem, "You are wonderful just the way you are." But when educators become overly-concerned with students' self-esteem, they are reluctant to demand high performance. And this decrease in high standards and performance is at the very heart of our academic problems.

Is Self-Esteem the Answer?

In many of the schools that are hooked on the self-esteem movement, academic content is watered down and tests are frowned upon because a low grade might lower a child's self-esteem. After all, how could a teacher tell a student that she earned a grade of C when other students received A's? A growing number of businesses have instituted training programs designed to raise employees' self-esteem. People with high opinions of themselves, they believe, will become more productive and amiable on the job.

When I first heard of this self-esteem-now approach, I began to implement the recommended ways to improve students' self-esteem. It wasn't long before I realized that high self-esteem was not the long sought-after answer that people believed it to be. Through surveys and personal observation, I was shocked to discover that the correlation between high self-esteem and achievement appeared to be *zero*. Students who seemed to have low self-esteem did just as well as students exhibiting high self-esteem in all of my math and computer classes.

My observations were confirmed by scientific findings when, in 1989, the California Task Force commissioned a group of researchers to test the relationship between self-esteem and performance and found none.

Surprise, Surprise

In their report titled, *The Social Importance of Self-Esteem*, many experts - to the shock of the task force and other supporters - concluded, "there is a paucity of good research, especially studies that could link the abuse of alcohol and drugs with self-esteem. The news most consistently reported however, is that the associations between self-esteem and its expected consequences are mixed, insignificant or absent." (Mecca, Smelser and Vasroncellos, 1989, *The Social Importance of Self-Esteem.*)

Self-esteem could not be shown to influence school grades, abuse of drugs and alcohol, child abuse, crime and violence or teen pregnancy. To add insult to injury, two studies linked high self-esteem with promiscuity among teens. Across multiple studies, the correlation between grades and self-esteem has been found to be negligible. And even when there is a correlation between high grades and high self-esteem, we can't be sure if it is high self-esteem that brings about high grades, or if the high grades bring about greater self-esteem.

Contrary to popular belief, the current research data strongly indicates that as a nation we are not suffering from low self-esteem as much as we are by *inflated* self-esteem. In a recent international test, the most rigorous and comprehensive ever conducted, the United States scored near the bottom - 19th out of 21 nations in math, and 16th out of 21 in science. Yet, incredibly, when tested for degree of self-esteem, the American kids scored near the top! (U.S.

Department of Education, National Center for Education Statistics, *Pursuing Excellence*, Table A 2.2.)

The Dark Side of Self-Esteem

In an eye-opening study reported in the *Journal of Personality and Social Psychology* (Colvin, Block and Funder, 1995), the authors discovered that repeated unearned praise creates inflated self-esteem which in turn causes a whole range of obnoxious behavior. These people tend to interrupt conversations and talk at, rather than to, people. One who has inflated self-esteem is often "conceited and quick to assert his or her own wants but lacks genuine regard for others."

In a related study, Roy F. Baumeister, professor of psychology at *Western University* in Cleveland, Ohio, reviewed hundreds of studies on self-esteem and came up with some surprising conclusions. He found that the notion that low self-esteem causes violence is simply untrue. All the evidence points to the fact that people like Adolph Hitler and Saddam Hussein, as well as the mugger or child bully, do not typically suffer from low self-esteem. In fact, just the opposite is true.

A Time Bomb

Baumeister discovered that it is "high self-esteem that is closer to the violent personality." (Baumeister, Smart and Boden, 1996, *Psychological Review*, Vol. 103, No. 1.) He found "the main recipe for violence is threatened egotism," that is, a belief in personal superiority that is challenged or questioned by another person. When a person having inflated self-esteem is rejected by a large proportion of the significant people in his life, look out. That person can become a time bomb just waiting to explode.

One could argue that a person who registers high on the self-esteem scale might in reality have a very low opinion of himself, or vice-versa. But this possibility is usually factored into these tests in order to ensure the tests' accuracy and validity. Every once in a while, a study does seem to link low self-esteem to antisocial or criminal behavior. But even then, there is disagreement concerning which came first, the bad behavior or the low self-esteem.

If a high-school dropout is convicted of drug possession and assault, and is found to have low self-esteem, what does it prove? Isn't it possible that this offender, after being apprehended and exposed, would then experience a devastating blow to his or her self-esteem? It is certainly possible that this person's self-esteem fell only *after* being caught and exposed.

Healthy Self-Esteem

I am not saying that self-esteem is a bad thing. Those who suffer from extremely low self-esteem need help. Life is unusually difficult and painful for people with little or no self-worth. They feel lost and helpless in a hostile world. One of the greatest gifts a parent can give to a child is the gift of healthy self-esteem. And the best way to help them get it is to help them to help themselves.

Self-esteem is not created in a vacuum; it is always connected to values. If a person values his place within a street gang, then his self-esteem will increase as he behaves in ways the gang members respect and admire. In that dark world, deviant and criminal behavior would bring high self-esteem.

For this reason, I prefer to use the term *healthy self-esteem* rather than high self-esteem. One having healthy self-esteem feels good about himself for all the right reasons. It is not a result of unearned praise or immoral behavior, and it is not a prerequisite for learning and achievement. It is the *product* of it.

Self-Esteem and Happiness

In many ways, healthy self-esteem is like happiness; it is not something you can run after and obtain directly. Both are by-products of doing certain things correctly in your life. The happiest people are not always the wealthiest or best looking; nor are they the ones who make being happy their main goal in life. Happiness comes naturally as we are busy accomplishing worthwhile goals and doing all we can to stay strong in body, mind and spirit.

Like happiness, healthy self-esteem will creep up on you when you are actively engaged in making positive changes in the world; when you are honest, kind, helpful, and goal-oriented; when you are tough enough to take a fall and not give up; when you have found meaning and a purpose for living; and when you learn how to love. All these greatly increase your chances of acquiring healthy self-esteem. Life is not merely a matter of having and getting, it is a matter of being and becoming.

People possessing healthy self-esteem have a realistic opinion of their strengths and weaknesses. They can laugh at themselves before others do. They are more concerned with doing what's right rather than pleasing others. Basically, these people like themselves – flaws and all – because they know that in their pursuit of excellence, it is natural to make mistakes along the way.

People who have healthy self-esteem are able to forgive others when wronged. When they make a mistake they forgive themselves but resolve to do better the next time – and they do. They know that being good is more important than being rich, and that doing the right thing is the best way to move toward lasting happiness.

The Benefits of Healthy Self-Esteem

People who have healthy self-esteem are more willing to take risks. The more risks we take, the greater the likelihood we will eventually succeed at what we are attempting. Research has shown that a common trait shared by super achievers is that they try but fail more often than those who accomplish little. These people view failure as just another lesson to be learned. They are not discouraged by setbacks but are challenged by them. They are not afraid to get off their butts and begin a new project. They know it is not possible to discover new oceans unless one has the courage to leave the shore.

> *To reach our destination we must sail- sometimes with the wind and sometimes against it. But we must sail and not drift or lie at anchor.*
> *- Oliver Wendell Holmes*

Another advantage of having healthy self-esteem is that one will tend to have positive self-expectations. And having positive expectations, as we have seen, can lead to self-fulfilling prophecies. Studies have shown that having a strong belief that you can succeed in a particular area and having the willingness to work hard, is more important than possessing the particular skills or talents commonly associated with that area.

People with healthy self-esteem are more fun to be around. They tend to be more popular because they spend less time trying to convince others how wonderful they are. Is there anything more boring than hearing someone go on and on about his or her talents and great achievements? People having healthy self-esteem are less concerned about themselves and more concerned with helping others.

How to Improve Your Self-Esteem

Through my observations and experiences with my children, students and friends, I have learned that there is one thing that will increase a person's self-esteem more than anything else – it is accomplishment. Whether it's getting an **A** on an exam, helping a friend through a crisis, getting a job promotion, or learning to love someone who is not especially lovable, nothing will develop healthy self-esteem more than setting a worthy goal and working hard to achieve it.

Healthy self-esteem is the *result*, not the *cause* of effort and achievement. If you love your job, you are fortunate. If you love what you do, you're probably good at it, and doing a good job will almost always increase your self-esteem.

Goal achievement is not totally dependent upon intelligence and ability. Reaching goals is more a matter of attitude than it is aptitude. Since we all have a conscience (the inner sense of what is right and wrong), deep down inside we know if our goal is worthy or not. One who works hard and pulls off a successful bank robbery might gain a false sense of self-esteem, but the goal was not worthy, and therefore the self-esteem will not be healthy.

Be Excellent - Wherever You Find Yourself

Normally, doing that which is good, noble, or self-sacrificing will improve your self-esteem. Healthy self-esteem and virtue are closely related. This is why, as we have seen, researchers continually report a very high correlation between altruistic service and one's self-esteem. Want to feel better about yourself? Figure out a way to share someone else's burden or join an organization that meets regularly to assist others in need.

And if family or professional obligations are currently preventing you from regular altruistic service, simply turn to the people closest to you and start there. Wherever you are, you can make a difference. Whether it's a telephone call, an offer to help a friend in time of need, or a simple smile and a warm "hello," you can give something. Kindness to others, with little regard to "what's in it for me?" will energize you, improve your immune system, and warm your soul.

He who gives, lives; He who does not, does not.
                                        - The Talmud

We make a living by what we earn, but we make a life by what we give.   - *Winston Churchill*

Your Physical Appearance and Self-Esteem

There are very few people in the world who are completely satisfied with their physical appearance. If people could simply wave a magic wand and change their appearance, virtually everyone would change something about the way they look. Most of us have learned to live with our poor complexions, large noses, expanding waist lines, and receding hairlines.

However, some people are downright embarrassed by their appearance. If you hate the way you look, your self-esteem is probably low. The good news is that most of the people who fall into this category can do something about it. Placing a warm smile upon your face will improve your appearance tenfold.

You may not be able to change the size of your nose or the number of wrinkles on your face, but you can keep yourself clean and well groomed. The number one cause for people's dissatisfaction with their appearance is obesity – something many of us can change.

Losing Weight

With the exception of a few Pacific islanders, Americans are the fattest people on the planet. In fact, the U.S. is probably the chubbiest society the world has ever known. Next to smoking, obesity claims more lives than any other health factor. According to the *Centers for Disease Control and Prevention,* excess weight contributes to cardiovascular disease (heart attacks, high blood pressure, and strokes), breast cancer, diabetes and other serious diseases, resulting in approximately 300,000 premature deaths within our country alone!

So what's the secret to losing weight and keeping it off? Why do so many of us try and fail? Actually, there is no secret. To lose weight, we all know what to do, we must reduce the number of calories we ingest and increase the number of calories we expend. The best way to decrease the intake of calories is to eat more nutritionally, and the best way to expend calories is to be more active and exercise. The reason you know what to do but don't do it is because it is not easy – it requires sustained effort and discipline.

How to Learn to Love Exercise

Fortunately, exercising becomes less difficult over time because it eventually becomes part of your life style. Changing your life-style to include diet control and exercise is the key to permanent weight loss. Crash diets (heavy weight loss in a short amount of time) never work; in fact soon after you stop this kind of diet, you will almost certainly gain all the weight back.

Basically, there are two types of exercise: aerobic and weight training. As mentioned earlier, aerobic exercise invigorates the circulatory and respiratory systems. Activities such as walking, jogging, swimming, and bicycling will burn calories and, as an added bonus, release endorphins.

Weight training strengthens muscles and increases the metabolic rate. In a study led by Wayne Westcott, Ph.D., the strength-training consultant for the national YMCA, it was discovered that people who engaged in 15 minutes of aerobic exercise *and* 15 minutes of weight training three times a week for two months, lost more than twice as much fat as those who did 30 minutes of aerobic exercise during the same period.

Exercise and Self-Esteem

Virtually everyone who exercises on a regular basis will tell you the same thing - exercising, or an active life-style, boosts self-esteem. Empowered living is facilitated by an active life style and exercise. Studies have shown that of those who exercised primarily to lose weight, the large majority felt better about themselves whether they lost the weight or not. There are many reasons for this but one of them has to do with the positive effects of setting and making progress toward a worthy goal. Earlier, I mentioned *noble goals*, goals that are always attainable because the one setting them is totally in charge of the outcome. You can begin to lose weight by setting a noble goal.

A Noble Goal

Eight years ago, I started an exercise program and improved my eating habits because I wanted to have more energy and lose some weight. I began to exercise on an apparatus that simulates cross-country skiing. Since my goal was to lose about ten pounds, I became frustrated when after several weeks of dieting and exercising, I didn't lose a pound.

I then shifted my focus onto a noble goal. My goal became: "While being careful about my diet, I exercise on the ski apparatus for 30 minutes at least four times a week. I do this for six months." Wording the goal in this way allowed me to concentrate on those actions I could control. Notice, no mention was made of the ultimate goal; only what I had to do each day.

I experienced a sense of pride and accomplishment after

each half-hour workout. I became less concerned about my ultimate goal of losing weight. Instead, I focused my attention on exercising one day at a time. My attitude quickly changed and my self-esteem improved.

It took several more weeks but eventually my weight decreased and my energy level increased. I've been exercising regularly ever since. I will either jog, walk, "ski," or use weights. To avoid boredom, I usually combine two or more of these activities in one session. I've been able to keep my weight within acceptable limits and my health has improved in many other ways.

Exercise - 100 Benefits

Over the years, I've discovered a highly effective way to motivate my students and seminar participants to begin an exercise program. I simply give them a copy of **100 Ways** - a comprehensive list describing 100 outstanding benefits of exercising. After reading the list, most people confess to feeling "guilty" or "uncomfortable" about being inactive. They find that the benefits described have a tremendous motivating effect because they far outweigh the inconvenience. I hope this list will do the same for you.

---

100 WAYS EXERCISE WILL ENRICH
THE QUALITY OF YOUR LIFE

1. Increases your self-confidence and self-esteem.
2. Improves your digestion.
3. Helps you to sleep better.
4. Gives you more energy.
5. Adds sparkle and radiance to your complexion.
6. Enhances your immune system.
7. Improves your body shape.
8. Burns up extra calories.
9. Tones and firms up muscles.
10. Provides more muscular definition.
11. Improves circulation and helps reduce blood pressure.
12. Lifts your spirits.
13. Reduces tension and quells stress.
14. Enables you to lose weight and keep it off.
15. Makes you limber.
16. Builds strength.
17. Improves endurance.
18. Increases the lean muscle tissue in your body.
19. Improves your appetite for healthy foods.
20. Alleviates menstrual cramps.
21. Improves muscle chemistry.
22. Increases metabolic rate.
23. Improves coordination and balance.
24. Improves your posture.
25. Eases and can possibly eliminate back problems and pain.

26. Allows you to use calories more efficiently.

27. Lowers your resting heart rate.

28. Increases muscle size through an increase in muscle fibers.

29. Enables your body to utilize nutrients more efficiently.

30. Improves the body's ability to burn fat.

31. Strengthens your bones.

32. Enhances oxygen transport throughout the body.

33. Improves liver functioning.

34. Strengthens the heart.

35. Improves blood flow through the body.

36. Helps to alleviate varicose veins.

37. Increases maximum cardiac output due to an increase in stroke volume.

38. Increases the weight of the heart.

39. Increases heart size.

40. Improves contractile function of the whole heart.

41. Deters heart disease.

42. Decreases cholesterol.

43. Decreases triglycerides.

44. Increases total hemoglobin.

45. Improves the body's ability to remove lactic acid.

46. Improves the body's ability to decrease heart rate after exercise.

47. Increases the number of open capillaries.

48. Improves blood flow to the active muscles at the peak of training.

49. Enhances the functioning of the cardiovascular system.

50. Enhances the functioning of the respiratory system.

51. Improves efficiency in breathing.

52. Increases the lung

capacity.

53. Improves bone metabolism.

54. Decreases the chances of osteoporosis.

55. Improves the development of and the strength of connective tissue.

56. Increases strength of ligaments.

57. Enhances neuromuscular relaxation thus reducing anxiety and tension.

58. Enables you to relax more quickly and completely.

59. Alleviates depression.

60. Enhances clarity of the mind.

61. Improves emotional stability.

62. Makes you feel good.

63. Increases efficiency of your sweat glands.

64. Makes you better able to stay warm in colder environments.

65. Helps you to respond more effectively to heat in that sweating begins at a lower body temperature.

66. Improves your body composition.

67. Improves body density.

68. Decreases fat tissue more easily.

69. Helps you to achieve a more agile body.

70. Increases your positive attitude about yourself and life.

71. Alleviates constipation.

72. Increases the efficiency of utilizing oxygen.

73. Enables you to meet new friends and develop fulfilling relationships.

74. Enables you to socialize while you are getting in shape at the same time.

75. Helps you move past self-imposed limitations.

76. Gives you a great

appreciation for life as a result of feeling better about yourself.

77. Enables you to better enjoy all types of physical activities.

78. Makes the clothes you wear look better on you.

79. Makes it easier to exercise consistently because you like how you look and feel and don't want to lose it.

80. Gives you a greater desire to participate in life 100% and to take more risks as a result of increased confidence and self-esteem.

81. Improves athletic performance.

82. Improves the whole quality of your life.

83. Will probably add a few years to your life.

84. It is the greatest tune-up for the body.

85. Reduces joint discomfort.

86. Increases your range of motion.

87. Gives you a feeling of control or mastery over your life and belief that you can create any reality you want.

88. Stimulates and improves concentration.

89. Brings color to your cheeks.

90. Decreases appetite when you work out from 20 minutes to one hour before a meal.

91. Gets your mind off irritations.

92. Stimulates a feeling of well-being and accomplishment.

93. Invigorates the body and mind.

94. It's a wonderful way to enjoy nature and the great outdoors.

95. Increases the body's awareness of itself.

96. Reduces or precludes boredom.

97. Increases your ability to solve problems

98. Gives you a clear perspective on ideas, issues, problems, and challenges.

99. Releases blockages and limitations in thinking.

100. Affords you the opportunity to experience your fullest potential.

✦✦✦✦✦✦✦✦

Self-Esteem and the Ancient Writings

After reading the latest studies regarding self-esteem and personal growth, I decided to consult the world's quintessential guide for personal development - the Bible. Although the Bible tells us how to live correctly, it doesn't have too much to say regarding self-esteem. The Bible emphasizes the importance of good actions rather than having good feelings.

The prime reason we should feel good about ourselves is that God loved us into existence. As the children of Israel came out of Egypt, I believe one of the most significant events in the history of mankind took place. With the Egyptian army in hot pursuit, the Hebrew people became trapped by the army on one side, and the sea on the other. When Moses prayed for deliverance, God miraculously parted the waters of the Red Sea permitting the Hebrew people to cross on dry ground. When Pharaoh's men attempted to cross, the God of Israel demonstrated His awesome power:

> *Then the Lord said to Moses, "Stretch out your hand over the sea, that the water may come back upon the Egyptians, upon their chariots, and upon their horsemen."*

> *So Moses stretched forth his hand over the sea, and the sea returned to its wonted flow when the morning appeared; and the Egyptians fled into it, and the Lord routed the Egyptians in the midst of the sea.*

> *The waters returned and covered the chariots and the horsemen and all the host of Pharaoh that had followed them into the sea; not so much as one of them remained.*
>
> *- Exodus 14:26-28*

According to the Talmud (Bavli, Sanhedrin 3ab), "When the Egyptian armies were drowning in the sea, the Heavenly Hosts broke out in songs of jubilation. God silenced them and said, 'My creatures are perishing and you sing praises?'"

This story and the message it contains is repeated every year during the Passover Seder by millions of Jews all over the world. It is a beautiful message. It reminds us that God is merciful and that He loves all of His creations. Yes, in spite of all your imperfections and bad habits, God loves you.

We cannot love ourselves unless we love others, and we cannot love others unless we love ourselves. But a selfish love of ourselves makes us incapable of loving others.

-Thomas Merton

If you would be loved, be worthy of being loved.
                                                    - Ovid

✦✦✦✦✦✦✦✦

9

MODERN RESEARCH
VERIFIES ANCIENT WISDOM

Science without religion is lame, religion without science is blind.

- Albert Einstein

The door closed to good deeds opens to disease. Melancholy creates disease while happiness cures.

- The Talmud

$\mathcal{T}$he veracity of this quote from the Talmud concerning the connection between depression (melancholy) and disease, and happiness and healing, has already been established in earlier chapters. Like the Talmud, the Bible also contains excellent guidelines for wholesome living. Interestingly, recent scientific research is confirming that living a life that is "biblically-based" leads to many physical and psychological benefits.

Studies show that people who have a relationship with God and participate in religious activities tend to be healthier and happier. Psychiatrist and researcher David Larson summarized years of psychiatric literature and published a report in the *American Journal of Psychiatry*. Over 90 percent of the studies he examined backed up the view that **people having strong religious convictions, on the average, enjoy better health and live longer.**

For one thing, people of faith are more apt to avoid life-threatening activities, such as smoking, drug and alcohol abuse and other "risky" behaviors. The data Larson examined also proved that having a "strong religious commitment" was one of the best deterrents against committing suicide.

The research showed that those who rate the importance of religion as low, are seven times more likely to have abnormal diastolic blood pressure than those who rate religion as important. The scientific data, says Larson, indicates that those who regularly attend a place of worship are less likely to develop heart disease or high blood pressure, and require less hospital care. In short, having and practicing religious faith is good for you.

The Benefits of Marriage

He who finds a good wife finds a good thing.
- Proverbs 18:22

To the above proverb we must add "she who finds a good husband finds a good thing." The ancient writings provide matchless wisdom and counsel. High on the list of recommendations is the institution of marriage. According to recent findings, most adults are better off within marriage, than they are in any other relational state.

A study conducted at Washington State University found that "couples who cohabit have less healthy relationships than those who are married" (Jan E. Sets, *The Link Between Past and Present Intimate Relationships*, Journal of Family Issues).

A UCLA study found that "marriages preceded by cohabitation are 50 to 100 percent more likely to break up than those marriages not preceded by cohabitation. Marriages preceded by cohabitation experienced significantly more difficulty in subsequent marriages regarding adultery, both alcohol and drug abuse, and independence" (Michael D. Newcomb and P. Bentler, *Assessment of Personality and Demographic Aspects of Cohabitation and Marital Success*, Journal of Personality Assessment).

In his book, *Marriage Savers,* author Michael McManus reports "Of 100 couples who begin living together, 40 will break up before marriage. And of the 60 who marry, at least 45 will divorce. That leaves only 15 intact marriages out of the original 100 couples."

UCLA biobehavioral scientist, Dr. Robert Coombs, discovered through a review of more than 130 studies, that married people had much lower rates of alcoholism, suicide, psychiatric care, and higher rates of self-evaluated happiness. (Robert Coombs, *Marital Status and Personal Wellbeing, A Literature Review*, Family Relations)

A highly respected psychiatric study conducted by psychiatrist Lee Robins discovered that married people had a lower rate of severe depression than people in any other relationship.

Category	Percent Who Experienced Severe Depression
Married (never divorced)	1.5
Never Married	2.4
Divorced Once	4.1
Cohabiting	5.1
Divorced Twice	5.8

(L. Robbins and D. Reiger, *Psychiatric Disorders in America: The Epidemiologic Catchment Area Study,* New York: Free Press).

When Sex is Best

Research documented in an *American Demographics* report reveals that "broken marriages create stress, resulting in weight change, stomach upset, fatigue, appetite loss, headaches, nervousness, nightmares, difficulty in sleeping and tension." In fact, divorced men, says researcher J.J. Lynch in *The Broken Heart: The Medical Consequences of Loneliness,* are twice as likely to die from heart disease, stroke, hypertension and cancer as married men in any given year.

The data also led to some surprising conclusions regarding sexual relations. Those who had the least premarital sex were more apt to report their marriage as "always warm and supportive." Also, the most religious women were most satisfied with the frequency of intercourse and were more orgasmic than were the nonreligious.

Research data reveals yet another way in which religious faith benefits people. Faith in a higher Power has been shown to be effective in healing lives that have been broken by addictions of all kinds.

The Twelve Steps

The power of faith to reform a life may not excite the secularists in our midst but the ability of religious faith to rescue lives that have been ravished by alcohol and drugs is irrefutable. In fact, one of the greatest spiritual movements of the twentieth century began in Akron, Ohio, on June 10, 1935, with the founding of *Alcoholics Anonymous,* or A.A.

When addicts and others who have experienced prolonged pain and hopelessness finally "hit bottom" and decide to change their lives, they often try self-help books, therapy groups and other forms of consciousness raising. After exhausting these resources, they come to the realization that the peace they seek is not to be found in those places. At this point, they are ready to accept the support and guidance of a higher Power. The acceptance and reliance upon a spiritual force outside of ourselves takes place when people work the *Twelve Steps* within A.A.

Light Breaks Through the Darkness

The beginnings of the A.A. movement is a remarkable story in itself. It began one day when two old friends arranged to meet. Ebby Thatcher, a surgeon, visited Bill Wilson (known as Bill W. in A.A.), who had been unemployed for years. Both men had something in common - both had been "hopeless alcoholics" for years.

At that meeting, Thatcher explained that he had recently had a religious experience and had yielded his life to God. He told Wilson - who had little interest in God or spiritual matters - that the desire to drink was gone and his life was changed. Although Wilson reluctantly accompanied Thatcher to a meeting at a New York rescue mission, he later went on a three-day binge and had to be hospitalized.

That night, as Wilson lay alone in his hospital bed - depressed and severely ill - he had an experience that would eventually change his life and the lives of millions of people around the world. As he described it:

I still gagged badly on the notion of a Power greater than myself, but finally, just for the moment, the last vestige of my proud obstinacy was crushed. All at once I found myself crying out, "If there is a God, let Him show Himself! I am ready to do anything, anything!"

Suddenly the room lit up with a great white light. I was caught up into an ecstasy which there are no words to describe. It seemed to me, in the mind's eye, that I was on a mountain and that a wind not of air but of spirit was blowing. And then it burst upon me that I was a free man.

A great peace stole over me and I thought, "No matter how wrong things seem to be, they are all right. Things are all right with God and His world."

Wilson was a new man. From that day on, he never took another drink. He went on to establish the Twelve Steps, a program which has become the most effective treatment for addictions of all kinds.

The first three steps of the Twelve Step program concern beliefs, the next nine concern action. The first three steps are:

1. We admitted we were powerless over alcohol - that our lives had become unmanageable.
2. Came to believe that a Power greater than ourselves could restore us to sanity.
3. Made a decision to turn our will and our lives over to the care of God, as we understand Him.

In the Belly of the Beast

Years ago, a very close friend of mine, whom I will call Adam, became desperate for an end to his battle with drug addiction. He decided to join a religiously based, Twelve Step program called *Teen Challenge*. A hardcore addict for over twenty years, he had been through countless detoxification and drug rehabilitation programs. On several occasions, he came close to death from either an overdose or some other mishap.

The night he was to be admitted into this residence program, Adam was sick and frightened. I was worried about his safety. I sensed that this was Adam's last chance to avoid destruction.

At that time, Adam was addicted to methadone and was a heavy smoker. Since the program did not allow the residents to smoke or take drugs of any kind, he would have to go through withdrawal "cold turkey." When I asked one of his counselors what would happen when Adam wanted a cigarette or some drug to lessen the pain that was about to attack his body, he said, "We will gather around him and pray for him and support him. Don't worry, I promise you he'll be all right."

When it came time to leave I looked into Adam's tear-filled eyes. I think we both shared the same thoughts. Adam had gone through so many attempts in the past to free himself from addiction and had gone through so much pain in the process, how would he ever get through this night and the next few days without the assistance of a doctor? Adam's fiancé and I left him that night not knowing what we would find when we returned to see him again three days later. (Outside contact with new residents is prohibited for at least three days.)

The Rebirth of a Man

When I saw Adam again, I was relieved to see that he had made it through the first three days without cigarettes or drugs. When I asked him how he was able to cope, he said, "I'm still very sick but the counselors are always there to help me. They prayed over me when I couldn't take it any more, and they told me how Jesus loved me and wanted me to be whole and well again. I feel like I now have a reason to live and I want to get better."

It has been over eight years since that fateful night and Adam is just fine. Through his new-found faith, courage and determination, Adam has not only survived but thrived. He is happily married to a wonderful woman who stuck by him and trusted in the Lord's power to heal. To this day, Adam gives God, the counselors at Teen Challenge, and the strength of his loyal wife the credit for helping him find his new life. Where every other rehabilitative program failed, this God-centered program succeeded.

The *United States Department of Health, Education and Welfare* studied various drug programs to determine their cure rates. The average cure rate for drug rehab facilities around the country is about 15 percent. The Study Director, Catherine B. Hess, discovered that Teen Challenge had an astonishing 75 percent cure rate for those students who graduate the full program. After extensive research, Dr. John A. Howard, a member of the *National Commission on Marijuana and Drug Abuse* reported, "Of all the drug programs reported to this commission, the most successful is the religious based program conducted by Teen Challenge."

Since the Twelve Steps of Alcoholics Anonymous were written in the 1930s, millions of people have not only stopped drinking and taking drugs but have become productive, contributing members of society. These programs span nations, cultures, religions, races and educational backgrounds. They have given hope to those who would otherwise be hopeless. They confirm the belief that a Power outside of ourselves can be instrumental in bringing people from the depths of despair to recovery and wellness.

Higher Expectations or a Higher Power?

The studies documented in this chapter demonstrate how faith and religious life can improve one's physical and psychological health and bring purpose to an otherwise meaningless existence. If you are lonely or depressed, faith in God can help restore your joy for living. If you are going through a difficult trial, a renewed spirit can provide the strength to carry on. If you have an addiction of any kind, reliance upon a higher Power has been shown to be the most effective way out of the enslavement. But these facts in and of themselves do not prove the existence of God.

The intelligent skeptic would say that the positive outcomes described above could be nothing more than manifestations of the placebo effect. The placebo, as you recall, is devoid of any real medicinal value. Its power comes from the fact that it deceptively inspires hope and raises expectations for healing. Patients who take placebos are helped because they have come to believe that they will be helped.

Studies in *expectation theory* have shown that people tend to say and do what they think is expected of them. For example, if a drug counselor can convince the addict that he is going to gain victory over drugs and become free of its demands, the addict, believing the counselor, is more apt to do so. Whereas in the past the addict could not conceive of being drug-free, he is now able to do it because he *believes* he can do it. In the same way, believing in an all-powerful and beneficent God could bring about similar "miracles" in a person's life.

The ability of a dominant figure in a relationship to raise the expectations of others in that relationship has tremendous ramifications. It is what makes a parent, teacher, doctor, or friend capable of helping those in their charge. It is what makes the impossible, possible. Similarly, the believer who has faith in a God who helps and heals *will* be helped and healed.

So what causes healing? Is it higher expectations, a higher Power, or *both*? I believe it is both, but there is no place for speculation in science. The scientist must ask, "Is this true cause and effect? Is this inference or fact? Is God real, or a human construct?" Although these questions cannot be answered conclusively, the sincere spiritual aspirant must ask them. These fascinating questions and others will be explored in the chapter entitled *The Fingerprint of God.*

Religion, I believe, is the most important component of a well-lived life, because it points out the meaning of life and - by teaching the values of cooperation, sacrifice, compassion and love - provides a pathway to God.   - Dr. Laura Schlessinger

There is a kind of nourishment our souls crave, even as our bodies need the right foods, sunshine, and exercise. Without that spiritual nourishment, our souls remain stunted and underdeveloped.
                    - Harold Kushner

❖❖❖❖❖❖❖❖

10

IS ANYONE REALLY LISTENING?

Let me not pray to be sheltered from dangers but to be fearless in facing them. Let me not beg for the stilling of my pain but for my heart to conquer it. Let me not crave in anxious fear to be saved but hope for the patience to win my freedom.

- Rabindranath Tagore

$\mathcal{C}$an praying really change anything? An increasing number within the medical community believe that it can. Scientific studies have shown that prayer can help patients heal.

In 1988, a California cardiologist conducted a 10-month study involving 393 cardiac care patients. He divided the patients into two groups; one group was prayed for by home prayer groups, while the other was not. Neither the patients, doctors or nurses knew which group the patients were in. The results were quite surprising. The patients who were prayed for were five times less likely to need antibiotics and three times less likely to develop pulmonary edema (fluid in the lungs).

After a careful review of that study, Larry Dossey, M.D., a Dallas internist, began a five-year quest to determine whether "this study stood alone or if there were other things out there." He gave up his medical practice, moved to New Mexico and examined over 130 scientific studies involving the effects of prayer.

Words That Heal

Dossey summarized his findings in his fascinating book, *Healing Words,* published by Harper Collins. He claims that "Experiments have shown that prayers positively affected high blood pressure, wounds, heart attacks, headaches, and anxiety."

Whereas some studies involved human subjects, other studies (where there were fewer and less difficult variables) involved viruses, bacteria and other life forms. Depending on the "prayers" being offered, some of these forms grew faster, while others grew slower. In one study he reviewed, 10 participants focused their thoughts on inhibiting the growth of laboratory fungi and 151 of 194 cultures showed retarded growth. In related studies, the same results were obtained even though the ones "praying" were 15 miles from the fungi.

According to Dossey, "The evidence is simply overwhelming that prayer functions at a distance to change physical processes in a variety of organisms, from bacteria to humans. Nothing seemed capable of stopping or blocking prayer. There's some aspect of the psyche that's nonlocal in space and time - immortal, eternal and omnipresent. This is why I think that these studies constitute empirical, indirect evidence for the existence of something we in the west have called a soul." Dossey goes so far as to suggest that physicians who don't pray for their patients are guilty of "spiritual malpractice."

> *Call to Me, and I will answer you, and I will tell you great and mighty things, which you do not know.*
>
> — Jeremiah 33:3

The Mystery of Prayer

There are so many unanswered questions concerning prayer. Does God really answer our prayers? And if so, how does He answer? Can we twist God's arm and convince Him to act? How do we get God to heal a dying child, or revive a failing marriage or bring peace and harmony to a sinking nation?

We are told that, *"The prayers of a righteous man can accomplish much."* - James 5:16b. But the Bible is replete with accounts of faithful servants of God who asked God to work in specific ways, only to see their requests denied. How can anyone get excited about this kind of experience? It's like a mystical crap-shoot. We are told to pray, but when we do, we can never be sure if, or how, God will answer. When it comes to prayer, there don't seem to be any guarantees.

When a prayer goes "unanswered," does it mean that the prayer was unsuccessful? A successful or righteous prayer is difficult to judge. I believe a prayer can be "successful" and still not bring about the intended results. Certainly, when we rattle off a series of wishes from a "shopping list" of requests, nothing is accomplished.

But when one has pure motives, prays with passion and has faith in a God who is capable of answering prayer, I believe God listens and responds. When these three elements are present - purity of motive, passion and faith - I believe the prayer will be heard; it will be "effective." However, we can never judge a prayer's effectiveness by whether or not it brings about that which is prayed for. We don't know when He will answer or how He will answer.

The Peace That Surpasses All Understanding

Although you can never be certain as to how God will answer your prayer, you can be confident of one thing - fervent praying will always help you in some way. As mentioned earlier, how and when God answers prayers is His business, but when we come to God and unload our feelings, when we express our fears, frustrations and hopes, we are helped psychologically. This unloading will often bring about an inner peace that "surpasses all understanding." One usually comes away with the feeling that, "Somehow everything is going to be all right, God has everything under control."

Whenever you wonder why God does not always answer your prayers, consider this:

I asked God for strength, that I might achieve, I was made weak, that I might learn humbly to obey. I asked for health, that I might do greater things, I was given infirmity, that I might do better things. I asked for riches, that I might be happy, I was given poverty, that I might be wise. I asked for power, that I might have the praise of man, I was given weakness, that I might feel the need for God. I asked for all things, that I might enjoy life, I was given life, that I might enjoy all things. I got nothing that I asked for - but everything that I hoped for.

Almost despite myself, my unspoken prayers were answered. I am, among all people, most richly blessed.

- Anonymous

Prayer Never Fails

So what is gained when you pray? To repeat, prayer eventually helps the one who prays. If you pray believing that God is there, if the prayer is passionate and sincere, God will respond. When you commune with God, you remind yourself that you are not alone in a cold and meaningless universe. When you pray, you come into God's presence and affirm that He listens and wants what's best for you. We can't know how He will answer our prayers or when He will answer them, but we can be certain that in His own mysterious way, He understands, empathizes, and wants us to succeed - according to *His* definition of success.

When we pray, we feel we are in the presence of a Force that is beyond our understanding yet is inconceivably good. We are reminded that the evil that exists in this world is the result of our having been given the gift of *free will*. If we were not free to do both good and evil we would be no different than the robot or the radish - incapable of behaving in any other way than the way we were programmed.

When you pray, you remind yourself that you are *not* the captain of your own ship or the master of your own fate (as many self-help books would have you believe). In prayer, you acknowledge your weaknesses and your limitations. You ask for forgiveness and when you do, you can know for certain that when you repent, you will be forgiven. Unlike the secularists - who believe the answers to all of our personal and social problems lie within us - you accept the fact that you can't do everything on your own.

I realize that some of you are struggling with this question. You would like to believe that there is a God who heeds your prayers, but since you don't have any direct proof, you remain unconvinced. Some of you are honestly searching for an answer. How, you ask, can anyone in this age of reason and science come to accept a supreme Being? In the next chapter, we will take a look at some of the reasons why an intelligent, rational person need never be embarrassed to say that there are viable arguments for the existence of God.

God, grant me the serenity to accept the things I cannot change, the courage to change the things I can, and the wisdom to know the difference.
                                        - Reinhold Niebuhr

✢✢✢✢✢✢✢✢

11

THE FINGERPRINT OF GOD

God does not play dice with the universe. He is subtle but he is not malicious.

- Albert Einstein

Let us weigh the gain and the loss in wagering that God is. Consider these alternatives: if you win, you win all; if you lose, you lose nothing. Do not hesitate, then, to wage that He is.

- Blaise Pascal

The most important answer for all humankind is the answer to the question, "Does God exist?" The believer states that there is a God; the atheist boldly states that God does not exist; the agnostic doesn't know - resigned to the fact that there simply is not enough evidence to know for certain.

If you already are a believer, this section will provide you with valuable information to share with a friend or loved one who is having difficulty believing that there is a God. However, if *you* are struggling with the question of God's existence, it is my hope that the facts presented in this chapter will open your mind to possibilities you may have never considered before.

The Cosmological Argument

From earliest times, one of the strongest arguments for the existence of God has been the *cosmological argument*. This argument addresses the fact that the universe is here and therefore must be explained in some way. It starts with the present universe and goes back to its beginning. It attempts to answer the question, "Since the universe is here, how did it get here?"

The law of *cause and effect,* which states that every material effect must have an adequate cause, is integral to the cosmological argument. By definition, a cause is that which has an effect; that is, every effect has had something which caused it. We know of no effect that is without a cause. Causes always precede an effect. The birth of a child is preceded by insemination; the dawn of a new day is preceded by the rising sun.

The law of cause and effect also states that every material effect must have an *adequate* antecedent cause. That is, the cause is always qualitatively and quantitatively superior to the effect. A space ship's ascent into the heavens cannot be caused by a catapult; a bucket of water cannot put out a forest fire, (but a torrential downpour can). And so we must ask, "What could have possibly caused the universe?"

Possible Causes of the Universe

The universe could have three possible causes:

1. The universe was created out of nothing; there was no cause - it just happened.
2. The universe is eternal; it had no beginning and it will have no end. It always was and always will be.
3. The universe had a beginning and was created by something or someone superior to it.

Let's examine each possibility.

The Universe Came From Nothing

Virtually no reputable scientist today believes that the universe created itself. No material object has ever created itself. Since the dawn of time, we have no instance of anything popping into existence on its own accord. The *first law of thermodynamics*, also known as the law of the conservation of energy, states that neither matter nor energy can be created or destroyed.

Matter can be converted into energy, and vice versa, but the total amount of all matter and energy in the universe will remain unchanged - forever. Nothing comes from nothing. Everything there ever was has been caused by something. The universe could not have possibly created itself; the notion that it did is simply absurd.

The Universe is Eternal

This theory states the universe always was, and always will be. If the universe always existed, we would not need to find a first cause. If it was always here, there would be no need for a creator. However, this theory violates one of the most established and revered scientific facts - the *second law of thermodynamics*. This law states that all systems (rivers, machines, and people) tend to decay and disintegrate over time. They experience a net increase in what is called *entropy* - a state of randomness or disorder. That is, any system left to its own devices always tends to move from order to disorder. The human body, for example, grows, matures, ages and dies. As we age, our bodies experience entropy. They go from order to disorder; they "wind down" until all systems fail and eventually stop.

Scientists agree that the universe is "running down" and will one day "die" - similar to an alarm clock that was initially wound up and left to wind down. Since it is running down, there was a time in the distant past when the universe was fully wound up - at the Beginning. Since anything that is eternal cannot wind down, the universe can not be eternal.

The Grand Designer

As we have seen, the universe did not create itself; nor is it eternal. The only remaining possibility is that the universe was created. Since the universe is an effect, it had to have an adequate cause or Creator which preceded it. This brings us to another argument for a Creator - the argument of design.

The *argument of design* states that all sophisticated or

highly-ordered objects, from an abacus to a zygote, came into being by an intelligent designer and implies a purpose or direction behind that design.

As an example, imagine you are walking in a forest and you happen to find a small triangular-shaped stone in the shape of an arrowhead. You might conclude that the stone "just happened"; perhaps it was shaped by the wind and water over time. Now let us assume you continue upon your journey and one day stumble upon a complete and functional bow and arrow.

What would you think? You would not know how they got there but you would have no choice but to conclude that someone made them. Since they were too "sophisticated" or complex to have just "happened" over time, the bow and arrow had to have been designed; they had to have had a "cause."

Just as any thinking person would conclude that a bow and arrow could not have simply evolved over time, so too this highly-ordered, ultra-sophisticated universe and the well-designed life forms contained within it could not have simply come about by happenstance.

Compared to inorganic objects - such as rocks, coins, or Hula Hoops - biological systems like plants and koala bears are enormously complex. Indeed, some scientists estimate that the universe is at least ten billion orders of magnitude (that's 10 followed by ten billion zeros) *too small or too young* to permit life to be formed by natural processes. According to these scientists - some of whom are theists and some who are not - the earth has not been here long enough to permit life to form by "accident."

In his extremely well-researched book, *Nature's Destiny*, scientist Michael Denton - Ph.D., medical doctor, and the Senior Research Fellow in Human Molecular Genetics at the

University of Otago in New Zealand - claims that all the research data, from physics to chemistry to biology, points to a designer whose goal for the cosmos was and is human life. Quoting from his book:

> *Whether one accepts or rejects the design hypothesis, whether one thinks of the designer as the Greek word soul or the Hebrew God, there is no avoiding the conclusion that the world looks as if it has been uniquely tailored for life: it appears to have been designed. All reality appears to be a vast, coherent, teleo-logical whole with life and mankind as its purpose and goal.*

Building on the work of some of the most prominent biologists, chemists, and physicists around today, Denton marshals a stunning range of scientific evidence to arrive at his inevitable conclusion: life is not a mere product of time and chance, but that it was intentionally *designed* for human beings. That is, the laws of nature are fine-tuned to reach a single endpoint - mankind.

For over four hundred years, science has been "the great ally of atheism and skepticism," says Denton. But now, at the dawn of the new millennium, the relentless stream of new scientific discoveries is pointing to the inescapable conclusion that "the cosmos is a specially designed whole with life and mankind as its fundamental goal and purpose."

As Denton and others continue their research into the next century, many in the science world are predicting that the wall which presently separates science and God will begin to crumble. As a "*cause,*" time and chance are simply inadequate to explain the effect of something so incredibly complex as the universe. The existence of the universe implies a Designer, or First Cause. And if the universe was created, it had to have a beginning.

The Big Bang

The most commonly accepted theory in astrophysics today is that the universe has a birthday - the *Big Bang*. In 1946, George Gamow, a Russian-born scientist, proposed that the universe was created sometime between 10 billion and 20 billion years ago from a cosmic explosion that hurled matter in all directions.

The theory also states that all the galaxies were created at that moment and are now rushing away from each other at the speed of light. That is, the earth has not existed forever as some believe, but was, according to this theory, created on a particular "day" - just as the Bible (and no other religious book) declares in the first chapter of Genesis.

Cosmologists tell us that something caused that initial explosion of what has been called a "primeval atom," or an intense concentration of "pure energy." Since scientists don't know who or what caused that first big bang and since they have no hard "evidence" for a personal God, many of them remain atheists or agnostics. But not all. With the recent astonishing discovery of the *Bible Code*, which will be covered in the next section, an increasing number of scientists are actually coming to believe in a Creator.

It's Like Looking at God

In 1992, observations made by a NASA team have moved the Big Bang theory from a consensus view to the nearly unanimous view among cosmologists: *there was an origin to the universe approximately 15 billion years ago.* In awe of what he was seeing as he peered through a telescope, George Smoot, a leader of the research team declared, "It's like looking at God." After studying NASA's conclusions, science-historian Frederick Burnham stated "These findings, now available, make the idea that God created the universe a more respectable hypothesis today than at any time in the last 100 years."

In the beginning God created the heavens and the earth. And the earth was without form, and void; and darkness was upon the face of the deep; and the Spirit of God was moving over the surface of the waters.

- Genesis 1:1-2

To this point, no mention has been made concerning the *nature* of this Creator, only that there are reasonable arguments for His existence. To begin to understand the Creator's nature, we turn to what is arguably one of the most remarkable discoveries of this century - the *Bible Code*.

The Bible Code

In the 18th century, a prominent Lithuanian rabbi, Elijah Solomon, known as the *Vilna of Gaon*, made a startling claim concerning the Bible. Consistent with the ancient teachings of **kabbalah** - the Jewish mystical tradition - he said:

> *All that was, is, and will be unto the end of time is included in the* **Torah,** *the first five books of the Bible. And not merely in a general sense, but as to details of every species and each one individually and details of everything that happened to him from the day of his birth until his end.*

He meant this literally; encoded within the surface words of the Bible, were *hidden* words providing detailed information about modern day events.

The Great Ones

In 1988, an Israeli, Dr. Eliyahu Rips, a world-class mathematician and one of the world's leading experts in group theory, revealed what he claimed to be a Bible Code. Along with a team of scientists, Rips found encoded within Genesis, the names of 32 of the so-called "great ones," or Great Sages in Jewish history; and in close proximity to each name was that person's date of birth or death.

These men all lived and died thousands of years *after* the Torah was given to Moses on Mount Sinai. Incredibly, the odds of these names and dates appearing in any text simply by chance were found - through statistical analysis - to be less than 1-in-50,000.

Rips used one of the simpler methods of decoding, a method known as *equidistant letter sequences*, or ELS. Starting with any letter in the text, he would skip a certain number of letters - three, or seven, or ten, or whatever - then count the next letter; skip an equal number of letters and use the next letter, and so on. Eventually, a word would be spelled out.

In his eagerly-anticipated book, *The Bible Code*, New York Times bestseller Michael Drosnin demonstrates how ELS works by using the following example:

<u>R</u>ips <u>e</u>xpl<u>a</u>ine<u>d</u> tha<u>t</u> eac<u>h</u> cod<u>e</u> is a <u>c</u>ase <u>o</u>f ad<u>d</u>ing <u>e</u>very fourth or 12th or 50th letter to form a word. Skip X spaces, and another X amount of spaces, and another X amount of spaces, and the hidden message is spelled out.

If you start with the first letter, "R" in the paragraph and skip the next three letters, the code will appear: **Read the code**. Words are found by skipping from 0 to any higher number of letters.

The Most Unique Book in the World

At this point you are probably thinking what any intelligent person would think: "Why, this is silly. Anyone working on a computer, if they searched long enough and used different skip sequences, could find *anything*!" There's only one problem with this argument. When researchers attempted to do just that - examine other large texts with a computer in an effort to find related words that were in close proximity (and more specifically, the names of the 32 sages and the appropriate dates) - they found absolutely nothing!

The identical search was carried out using other books: a

Hebrew-language translation of the novel, *War and Peace* (which is equal in length to Genesis), the Book of Isaiah, the Book of Genesis randomized by scrambling its verses, etc. Absolutely no evidence whatever of a relationship between names and their appropriate dates was found with these other books; the results were no different from what would happen by chance. How could the author of the Torah possibly have known about the lives of these men? What other information could possibly be hidden there?

Dr. Rips' research passed a high-level peer review and was published in *Statistical Science,* a highly-regarded journal of mathematics. As a professor who teaches both math and computer courses in college, I am familiar with the strict process by which all research findings are critiqued and verified by outside experts before they are eventually published in math journals. This article and its incredible implications opened an immediate firestorm within the scientific and religious communities that has yet to be extinguished.

Science Tests Faith

When Harold Gans, senior cryptologic mathematician at the Pentagon's *National Security Agency* heard about the startling discovery of hidden codes in the Torah, he dismissed it immediately, "It sounded so off-the-wall to me; I thought it was simply absurd." As one who is proficient in computer technology, Gans decided to replicate Rips' study in an effort to disprove it. In 1989, he wrote his own computer program and searched for the same information Rips and his team had discovered.

The results of his 440-hour study shocked this man of science. The names of men who lived hundreds and thousands of years after the Bible was written were encoded in detail along with their dates of birth or death. He calculated that the odds of this appearing by chance were less than 1-in-62,500. He was both amazed and ecstatic, "It sent a chill up my spine," said the Pentagon code-breaker. Gans became convinced the Bible code was real.

The people who have been involved in bringing the codes to light represent an unusual blend of the ancient and the modern, and the religious as well as the scientific. While some of the researchers started out being religious, some who were not, after investigating and verifying the authenticity of the codes, have abruptly changed their life course and embraced religion. Both Rips and Gans eventually left all their other pursuits to devote their full time to the study of the Torah.

The Assassin

If you were just looking for words, any words, you could find them in any sufficiently long book, particularly if you use a computer to find the words. But what you will find is generally random and unrelated. For example, finding the words: *house, book* and *run*, would not mean anything; these are just random words. But, if you found *declaration*, *independence, 1776*, and *United States* appearing together, you would have to conclude that their appearance was not mere happenstance.

To determine if a finding is random or is beyond what you would expect to find at random, you would have to apply a mathematical   technique known as *statistical analysis*.

Whether or not something is statistically significant depends on how many related terms are found in a small area of text, and how many letters are in each term. Short words in large amounts of text are very likely just a coincidence. But the presence of longer, related words in a small area of text indicates a high probability that they were intentionally coded there.

Incredibly, Dr. Rips discovered the following words, some before, and some just after the assassination of Israeli Prime Minister Yitzhak Rabin: *"Yitzhak Rabin,"* *"Amir,"* *"Name of assassin,"* *"Tel Aviv,"* and *"In 5756."* **Amir** is the name of the man who killed Rabin; **In 5756**, is the Hebrew date comparable to our 1995 - the year Rabin was killed in Tel Aviv. The probability of all these words appearing together by chance is close to zero.

One Hundred Seashells

To help you understand the concept of mathematical probability, imagine you are walking along a seashore when you spot four seashells in the sand that are positioned in the shape of a square. You probably wouldn't think too much of it. They may or may not have been purposely placed there.

You continue your little stroll when suddenly, you spot 100 seashells that clearly spell out the words: "*Life is beautiful!*" Hmmmm. The probability that this message was formed by chance would, like the example of Rabin's assassination, be many millions-to-one. There is virtually no chance the message spelled out by the seashells could not have been intentional. The only inescapable conclusion you could come to is that some form of intelligence *wrote* the message.

Hidden Messages From God

The following is only a small sample of the many astonishing hidden messages (some of which are presented in Dr. Jeffrey Satinover's excellent book, *Cracking The Bible Code*), that have been discovered in the Bible by Rips and others:

* "*Hitler*," "*Nazi*," and "*slaughter*" were all found in close proximity. "*Eichmann*," was found together with "*extermination*," and "*the ovens*."
* "*President Kennedy*," appears only once in the Bible; but close to his name the words, "*to die*," and "*Dallas,*" were also found. Where the name "*Oswald*" appears, the words "*sniper*," and "*marksman*" also appear.
* When "*Scuds*" was found in Genesis, the following words were also found close by: "*Russian*," "*missile*," "*Saddam*," "*Hussein*," "*3rd of Shevat*" (the date the war actually began), "*Schwarzkopf*," "*America*," and "*in Saudi Arabia*."

You can find "Nazi," or "America" in any large text, if not in *War and Peace*, then in some other large book. Sooner or later you will find some equidistant skip sequence that spells out virtually any word you target. But **only in the Bible** can you consistently find encoded - in close proximity - words that are related and describe events that have happened or are likely to happen. Except for the astonishing messages found in the Torah, the phenomenon is simply nonexistent.

The Critics

Will the evidence remain unrefuted? As of this writing, some of the world's most distinguished mathematicians and computer experts, most of them skeptics, have been involved in projects to examine and test the veracity of the codes. To this date, the codes have stood up to every test. The "fatal flaw" has not been found.

The story of the Bible Code, started at Mount Sinai, has been kept alive by the writings of kabbalists - the original cryptologists - and continues today with the research of scientists of the highest caliber. What if the present research holds up? What will it mean? If new research continues to confirm earlier findings, the codes could be the most significant discovery of this, or any other century.

After examining the Bible code research findings, I. Piatetski-Shapiro, a leading mathematician at Yale, remains convinced that the codes are "real"; that they do indeed contain names and events that took place long after the Torah was given to Moses, and that no other book on the face of the earth does the same. "As a mathematician, my instinct is that there is something here. I think that the only answer is - that God exists."

Another classic argument for the existence of God is the ability of the biblical prophets - who claimed that they were inspired by God Himself - to accurately and consistently predict the future.

Israel and the Prophets

Frederick the Great asked his wise men if they had a single, irrefutable proof of God. One of them came forward and answered, "Yes, your majesty--the Jews."

When I first read the story quoted above, I did not understand it. But that was before I learned about some of the biblical verses that pertained to the Jewish people and the nation of Israel.

Israel - the people and the nation - is a miracle of history. It has gone through experiences that are unlike anything even remotely experienced by any other nation in the history of the world. That these highly unusual events occurred *at all* is astonishing, but the fact that they were foretold by men who lived hundreds, and even thousands of years before the events took place points not only to the existence of God, but to a God who communicates with His people.

Let's take a look at some of these prophecies and their fulfillment. (Many examples could be cited for each prophecy, but only a small sample will be presented here.)

The first prophecy we will examine took place about 3200 years ago as the Hebrew people - who had just been released from slavery in Egypt - were on their way to the Promised Land. Moses stood before the people and made an ominous prediction. He told the people that at some time in the future, they would be attacked by a mighty power; their nation would be destroyed, and the survivors would be carried off into every corner of the earth.

And it shall come about that as the Lord delighted over you to prosper you, and multiply you, so the Lord will delight over you to make you perish and destroy you; and you shall be torn from the land where you are entering to possess it.

Moreover, the Lord will scatter you among all peoples, from one end of the earth to the other end of the earth; and there you shall serve other gods, wood and stone, which you or your fathers have not known.
                                    - Deuteronomy 28:63-64

Almost 700 years later, the first stage of this prophecy came to pass. One hundred and fifty years before the prophesied invasion actually took place, the prophet Isaiah clarified Moses' prediction and named the conquering power that would destroy Israel.

Behold, the days are coming when all that is in your house, and all that your fathers have laid up in store to this day shall be carried to Babylon; nothing shall be left, says the Lord.
                                    - Isaiah 39:6

And just a few years before the Babylonian invasion, the prophet Jeremiah predicted the exact length of time the Jewish captives would remain in exile. He also said that before the Jewish people would be allowed to return, Babylon would be destroyed by yet another world power.

And this whole land shall be a desolation and a horror, and these nations shall serve the king of Babylon seventy years.

Then it will be when seventy years are completed I will punish the king of Babylon and that nation,

*declares the Lord, for their iniquity, and the land of
the Chaldeans; and I will make it an everlasting
desolation.*

- Jeremiah 25:11,12

In 586 BC, precisely as prophesied, the Babylonians invaded the southern kingdom of Judah and destroyed Jerusalem and the Holy Temple. The survivors were taken captive into Babylon. The Babylonians were later conquered by the Persians. Cyrus, the Persian king, allowed the Jewish people to return to rebuild the Temple at Jerusalem. The Jews were held captive in Babylon for *exactly 70 years* - just as Jeremiah predicted.

The Crucifixion of the Jews

When Cyrus allowed the Jewish people to return to Palestine, they rebuilt the Temple and lived on the land until another destroyer appeared on the horizon. The second stage of Israel's chastisement occurred some 600 years later when Titus and his Roman legions sacked and destroyed Jerusalem. For the second time, the Temple at Jerusalem was destroyed. To this day, it has not been rebuilt.

Forty years before the invasion, Jesus accurately predicted the destruction of Jerusalem and the Temple at the hands of the Romans.

*...and they will fall by the edge of the sword, and will
be led captive into all the nations; and Jerusalem will
be trampled underfoot by the Gentiles until the times
of the Gentiles be fulfilled.*   - Luke 21:24

We learn from the writings of the famous Jewish historian, Josephus Flavius, that over one million Jews died in the siege that was placed around the holy city. Thousands of Jews were crucified. In his classic book, *The Story of Civilization,* historian Will Durant chronicles the horror that took place at that time:

> *The victors gave no quarter, but slew all Jews upon whom they could lay their hands; 97,000 fugitives were caught and sold as slaves; many of them died as unwilling gladiators in the triumphal games. Josephus numbered at 1,197,000 the Jews killed in this siege and its aftermath. Those that remained lived on the edge of starvation.*

With the second destruction of Jerusalem, Moses' prophecy regarding the world-wide dispersion of the Jewish people was completed. The Roman conquerors brought their captives into every province within their empire. The great *Diaspora* had begun; the dispersion became global. To this day, the "wandering Jew" can be found in virtually every corner of the world.

A People Scorned

When Moses told the Hebrew people that they would one day be attacked, destroyed and "scattered among all peoples," he also told them they would not find rest or security in the lands where their captors would take them.

*And among those nations you shall find no rest, and
there shall be no resting place for the sole of your
foot; but there the Lord will give you a troubling
heart, failing of eyes, and despair of soul.*

*So your life shall hang in doubt before you; and you
shall be in dread night and day, and shall have no
assurance of your life.*

- Deuteronomy 28:65-66

Speaking for the Lord, Jeremiah warned the people:

*And I will pursue them with the sword, with famine
and with pestilence; and I will make them a terror to
all the kingdoms of the earth, to be a curse, and a
horror, and a hissing, and a reproach among all the
nations where I have driven them.*

- Jeremiah 29:18

The ceaseless hatred and persecution of the Jewish people
down through the centuries is a sad historical fact. The Jewish
people have been maligned, scorned, persecuted, tortured and
killed on a scale unparalled in human history. No other ethnic
group has gone through the systematic terror and destruction
that the "chosen people" have endured over the centuries.

Jews have suffered during the Crusades, through
expulsions from their host nations, from the Spanish
Inquisition, from pogroms, and of course from the greatest evil
perpetrated on one people by another - the *Holocaust.* Again,
prophecy fulfilled.

The Only Time in History

Two of the most remarkable prophecies remain to be discussed. The first one involves a political event that has happened only once in history - the rebirth of a nation.

Before describing the fulfillment of this prophesy, let's turn our attention to the pronouncements of the ancient prophets.

> *And He will lift up a standard for the nations, and He will assemble the banished ones of Israel, and will gather the dispersed of Judah from the four corners of the earth.*
>
> - Isaiah 11:12

> *After many days you will be summoned; in the latter years you will come into the land that is restored from the sword, whose inhabitants have been gathered from many nations to the mountains of Israel which has been a continual waste; but its people were brought out from the nations, and they are living securely, all of them.*
>
> - Ezekiel 38:8

The fulfillment of these prophecies began on May 14, 1948 in Tel Aviv with the birth of the sovereign State of Israel. Many of the "banished ones" of Israel have returned "from the four corners of the earth." This rebirth marked an event without parallel in human history. Miracles surrounded this unprecedented event.

Immediately after the State of Israel was officially born, the five Arab armies of Syria, Lebanon, Egypt, Iraq and Jordan swooped down with the intent of driving the Jews into the sea. The Israelis had only 20,000 ill-prepared and under-equipped men to hold back 60,000 well-trained and well-armed invaders on five fronts. The world held its breath. It was only a matter of time. But whether you attribute the outcome to a ferocious will to survive or the intervention of God, or both, the Israelis not only held back their attackers, but went on to win new territory and expand their borders.

With each day, our generation has had the privilege to witness this prophecy unfolding before our eyes as Jews from around the world "have been gathered from many nations to the mountains of Israel." This is a prophecy in progress. No other race or ethnic group has ever lost their homeland and returned thousands of years later to reclaim it. Israel: the only nation to be reborn - exactly as prophesied.

Jerusalem - The Key to World Peace

The next prophecy concerns *Jerusalem*, the "City of Peace," and its critical role in the "last days." About 2500 years ago, after having been held captive in Babylon, the prophet Zechariah along with others, was allowed to return to Jerusalem to rebuild the ruined Temple. While there, he made a prophecy that must have sounded ludicrous to those who first heard it.

Behold, I am going to make Jerusalem a cup that causes reeling to all the peoples around; and when the siege is against Jerusalem, it will also be against Judah.

And it will come about in that day that I will make Jerusalem a heavy stone for all peoples; all who lift it will be severely injured. And all the nations of the earth will be gathered against it.
                                    - Zechariah 12:2,3

Zechariah prophesied that Jerusalem would one day be a "cup that causes reeling" to all the peoples living around her, and it would also be a "heavy stone" for *all* the people in the world. All who would attempt to "lift it" would be severely injured.

A cup that "causes reeling" is something which strikes fear in the hearts of others. Could you imagine the reaction of Zechariah's contemporaries upon hearing these words? The prophet made these pronouncements amidst the ruins of a "city" that was little more than a pile of rubble. How could such a pitiful place *ever* strike fear in the hearts of its neighbors? But again, history has confirmed this prediction.

David and Goliath

As much as her Arab neighbors have attempted to push Israel into the sea, they have been unable to do so. Since its birth in 1948, this small nation has withstood every attempt to annihilate her. Like David fighting Goliath, Israel has been victorious in all the wars that have been started by her Arab neighbors. And today because of her superior army and air power and her strong alliance with America, Israel is in an excellent position to defeat any hostile nation that might attack her.

The next part of the prophecy concerned *all* the nations of the world: "Jerusalem would become a heavy stone for all peoples...And all the nations would be gathered against it." Again, imagine the response of those who first heard this prophecy. How in the world could this burnt-out little hamlet ever become a "heavy stone," or problem to the entire world? Incredibly, this is exactly what Jerusalem is today.

To realize that this prophecy has been fulfilled, all one would have to do is read the daily newspaper. Given a list of cities: New York, Moscow, Peking, Rome, London, Baghdad and Jerusalem, which **one** city do you believe holds the key to world peace? There's absolutely no doubt! Jerusalem is universally perceived to be the prime political "powder keg."

A great majority of the nations and all of the world's leading powers have a vested interest in Jerusalem because of its religious significance. Christians and Jews revere this city as the most important holy place in the world. Muslims hold Jerusalem to be the third most holy place on earth.

If a war were to break out over this city, the warring factions would immediately be aided by their allies from around the world. The war would no doubt become global. All signs are pointing to Jerusalem as the most likely catalyst for the next world war - just as prophesied.

Quoting from the well-documented book, *A Cup of Trembling*, by historian Dave Hunt:

Certainly the prophesies of Jerusalem's ultimate importance seemed akin to madness as Jerusalem was repeatedly destroyed and then lay in ruins and all but abandoned for centuries. Yet today, in continuing fulfillment as further prophecies unfold, Jerusalem has indeed become a "cup of trembling" and a "burdensome stone" around the necks of all nations.

Armageddon - The Last War?

If prophecies up to this point have been 100 percent accurate, how likely is it that the prophecies that are yet future will also prove to be correct? Many Bible scholars believe that Jerusalem will be the spark that ignites this war of all wars, the last war - Armageddon. There are scholars from both the Christian and Jewish faiths who believe the scriptures are telling us that this great war will be accompanied by the most horrific natural disasters the world has ever experienced. They further believe that it is **our** generation that is now living in the "latter days" spoken of by Ezekiel and others.

Notice the sentence, *"And all the nations of the earth will be gathered against it."* At the time that Jerusalem is a "heavy stone" and a "cup of trembling" for all peoples (which is the case in our day), the nations of the world will be gathered against it, that is, poised to attack her.

As unlikely as it may appear to some, the "mother of all wars" may indeed be imminent. If the prophecies regarding the future turn out to be as accurate as the ones that have already come to pass (and there is no reason to believe they won't be), it's just one more reason for each of us to come to terms with the God who has clearly spoken to us through His prophets.

If Not God, Who?

If these prophets were not inspired by God, the question remains - how were they able to make the prophecies that have been described in this section come to pass? One explanation is - they didn't. Instead, some have argued, the prophecies were interjected into the Bible *after* the actual events took place. But anyone who is familiar with the incredibly meticulous methods the Jewish scribes have always used to transcribe the Bible (especially the Torah, the first five books of the Bible) knows that this possibility is extremely remote.

Another possible explanation is that the Jewish people, aware of the prophecies concerning them and their nation, simply made them happen. They believed that the prophecies were sent by God and expected them to happen. Over the centuries, these expectations provided the Jewish people with the will and the courage to behave in such a way as to bring about their fulfillment. According to this theory, the expectations became self-fulfilling prophecies.

Some have argued that the prophets were not inspired by God but instead had psychic abilities; that is, they had the gift of precognition.

In light of all the other corroborative evidence cited in this chapter, I find the alternative arguments described above harder to believe than the one that suggests that it was God who inspired these men to say what they said. Again, quoting from Dave Hunt's book:

The fact that what God inspired His prophets to declare in advance concerning Israel occurred precisely as foretold cannot be explained as a mere series of coincidences. These fulfillments could not have happened by chance. The probability of that happening is a mathematical impossibility. No honest person can dispute the facts or reject the conclusion to which they point so clearly.

To repeat, it is not possible to become convinced of God's existence through examination of the evidence alone. Ultimately, having a relationship with God is a matter of taking whatever faith you have and putting it into action. This action will take you upon a spiritual journey - a journey that is like no other.

✦✦✦✦✦✦✦✦

* * * * *

12

THE SPIRITUAL JOURNEY

*All that I have seen teaches me to trust the Creator
for all that I have not seen.*
                                        - Ralph Waldo Emerson

So how do you begin your spiritual journey? If you've already begun it, the question becomes, how do you *advance* along the Path? It has been said that a journey of a thousand miles begins with the first step. The first step is to make a commitment to the Lord of the universe.

Making a commitment to God is not only a decision of the mind - one in which you simply give mental assent and say, "I believe." A belief in God that does not change a life is meaningless. This decision must involve the heart and soul as well. When you make a commitment to God you acknowledge not only that He is real, but that He wants you and you belong to Him.

Commitment is knowing what you want in this world and committing yourself to doing everything in your power to remain obedient to Him. Your commitment is demonstrated by the way you live. You serve Him and are obedient to His commands, not because you are afraid of being punished or because you want to win a ticket to heaven, but because you love Him and are grateful for all He has given you. If you've been a slave to a particular habit, you decide once and for all to do something about it. And then you do it.

You come to realize that the most important command for all mankind is to "Love the Lord your God with all your heart, soul and might, and love your neighbor as yourself." You come to understand that your reason for being here is *tikkun olam* - a Hebrew term meaning "repair the world." Prayer, meditation, and the study of spiritual material become a routine part of your day.

Dare to Look Within

The first step after we make a commitment is to identify our sins. Whereas some sins are obvious, others are not as easy to identify. We live in a society which does not encourage introspection. We are normally not open to self-reflection in an effort to find out what's wrong with us. We would rather find out what's wrong with everyone else.

Do a quick self-examination right now. Do you enjoy knowing about other people's problems? Do you enjoy talking about them? We don't like to think about our own shortcomings and sins. We'd rather concentrate on the flaws of other people. But looking within ourselves is exactly what we must do if we want to succeed in life and become the people we are destined to become.

After we identify our sins and weaknesses, the next step is to do something about them. We do this through a process known as repentance.

A New Life

One can establish a relationship with God intellectually ("I believe") and emotionally ("I love You Lord"), but without true *repentance*, these are to no avail. True repentance is not just feeling sorry for your sins and asking God to forgive you. When you repent, you identify and feel disgust for your sins; you become emotionally involved to the point of doing something about them.

Whether you've committed a particular sin once or a hundred times, if you confess your sins and repent, God forgives you. But confession alone does not mean repentance has taken place. Repentance is a process which culminates in a changed life.

The Hebrew word for repentance is *teshuva*, the root of that word is *shuva* which means return. It is a returning to the true *Path*; it is a 180-degree turn toward the light. The person who repents of selfishness will become more charitable; the one who repents of habitual lying will become truthful; the person who had given up on life will begin to work toward worthy goals.

Many of God's greatest blessings follow on the heels of repentance. True repentance, however, does not take place until you devise an effective program of change so that you don't commit the sin again. If you are a gossip, you have not repented of gossiping until you stop the gossip. You have not repented of lying until you stop the pattern of lying.

Too often, we want to be forgiven but we do not want to give up the sin. We may even think it is "impossible" to stop the sinning, but God will stand by our side and empower us to do the right thing. Remember, He said He would never fail us nor forsake us.

The Ironman

I once read an article which included an interview with Mark Allen, winner of the *Ironman Triathlon* contest - arguably the most grueling athletic contest in the world. When asked what his recipe for success was, he said he had the habit of looking into himself in order to find at least one area where he could improve.

Once he identified something that was holding him back - whether it was physical, emotional or spiritual in nature - he created a program to make a change, no matter how small, in that particular area. When that behavioral change became a habit he moved on to the next change. You have to begin with that first small step. There is probably no better way to make changes and improve the quality of your life than in progressive steps, one step at a time.

Have the courage to look within and say, "I don't like what I see here; I'm going to change this. This is what I'm going to do about it starting today." Sometimes, you are able to conquer it right away and never do it again. More than likely, the problem will rear its ugly head again after a day, a month or a year. But continue to work at it, diminishing its frequency.

Whenever it tempts you, do not give in. This is how you advance spiritually. This is how you move toward excellence.

You Can't Always Trust Your Feelings

There are times when we should trust our instincts. But in our culture, how we feel - our moods - are given too much importance. Too often, people do only what they feel like doing. However, people of excellence and high character have learned to control their emotions. They have learned the importance of doing what is right whether they feel like it or not. They know that a good deed or loving act does not have to be heartfelt to be performed.

If God commands something, we shouldn't wait until we *feel* in the mood to do it. Since God commands us to be tolerant of others, the blessing comes when we act with tolerance. How we feel about it is irrelevant. When we live according to the principles prescribed by God, we not only honor Him, but in the process we do what is best for ourselves. **Cooperation with God is the wisest "self-help" action anyone could ever take.**

Can you imagine getting up each weekday morning and deciding whether or not to go to work based on how you feel that morning? If that were the case, you might have to find the nearest unemployment office. Instead, you go to work whether you feel like it or not. Similarly, the one who would grow in spiritual power will do the right thing whether he feels like it or not.

God commands that we love one another. Should you wait until you feel like loving before you act with kindness and consideration toward that "unlovable" person? No, just do it.

Be kind and considerate regardless of your feelings. When you do this, you might very well find yourself saying, "I didn't want to do this thing, I really didn't feel like obeying, but now that I did, I actually feel good about it." A good action that is initially performed "out of duty" has a way of becoming a heart response. In time, you will perform the act because you want to.

In order to make continued progress on our spiritual journey, we must learn to acquire another virtue - we must learn how to forgive.

The Incredible Power of Forgiveness

As long as you harbor hate or malice toward others, your soul can never be at peace. Your enemies - the ones whom you believe wronged you - win another victory over you every time you think about them and what they did to hurt you. Every time you dwell upon the injury they caused, you build another enemy outpost in your being and you are damaged physically, mentally and spiritually.

When you can't forgive, the harmful chemicals that are created because of your pent-up anger will cause you to suffer. Whether it's in your stomach, your back, your heart or your head, you *will* pay a price. Your "enemy" wins again. Don't allow this to happen to you. Forgive.

Also, we learn from God's word that until we forgive others, we cannot expect to be forgiven:

> *For if you forgive men for their transgressions, your*
> *heavenly Father will also forgive you. but if you do*

not forgive men, then your Father will not forgive your transgressions.

                                    - Matthew 6:14-15

This is a powerful statement - we will not be forgiven unless we first forgive others. If there is something gnawing away at you, a sense of guilt, or a feeling that you cannot explain or identify, it could be the result of your inability or unwillingness to forgive someone. The refusal to forgive another person will cause *you* to feel unforgiven and you may not even be aware of it.

The Answers Lie Within

John F. Kennedy once said, "Always forgive your enemies, but never forget their names." I guess this is good advice, especially in the world of politics. However, we must be careful; when we remember the person, we will usually remember the wrong that was done to us, making forgiving difficult.

It is not easy to forgive completely, even when the other person comes to us to ask for forgiveness. But the one who is spiritually advanced has learned to do something that is more difficult - forgive the other person *before* he or she even asks for forgiveness. The person who will have the most difficulty forgiving is the one whose heart is filled with pride.

If you think too highly of yourself, one way to acquire and maintain a more balanced opinion of who you are is to look within. If you have the courage to shine the light of truth upon all the junk you find there you will take great strides in your spiritual journey. Honest self-examination should help you to feel humble, not arrogant; unpretentious, not conceited.

When you begin to see that you are just chock-full of your own weaknesses and imperfections, you will become less vain; you will learn to *laugh* at some of the things that used to bother you, and you will find it easier to forgive others.

If you need help in forgiving, read the Bible verses in *Part II*, listed under the section, *Forgiveness*. God's words are powerful; they can pierce the darkest minds and coldest hearts. His words can help us when everything else has failed. Whenever you find yourself imprisoned by the walls of hate, envy, greed or fear, let God's word smash down those walls and set you free.

The Journey

Where do you stand today? Are you advanced on the Path or are you just starting out? Are you eating meat or are you still being nursed by milk? Perhaps you are looking down at the Path's beginning - afraid to take that first step. Most Americans either believe in God, or are agnostic. Yet, the large majority of us live as atheists. What do you think would happen if you were to live "as if" you believed?

One who spent a good portion of his life delving into these questions was the nineteenth-century Danish philosopher and religious thinker, Soren Kierkegaard - generally considered to be one of the founders of existentialism. Because of the absence of objective evidence, he believed that we could never be certain of God's existence.

For Kierkegaard, coming to God and being awakened spiritually was a matter of *obeying* God more than it was a matter of proving His existence through rational argument. Religion, he felt, is a matter of *doing* more than it is a matter of believing. He rightly understood that faith is meaningless unless it is translated into action.

Allow me to digress for a moment.

There is the well-known story about the elderly gentleman who decided to pray that he would win the lottery. Every night he would pray, "Lord I'm a good man; I take care of my family and I'm a God-fearing man, please let me win the lottery. I can sure use the money." He said this prayer every night for one whole year. Then one night he prayed with anger in his heart, "Lord, I can't understand this. I'm a good person; I take care of my family, I'm a good parent and an excellent husband. Why haven't you let me win the lottery?"

At that, a tremendous bolt of lightning appeared and thunder boomed from out of the darkened sky. Then, a loud voice filled the air, "Old man, at least meet me half way, BUY A TICKET!"

To advance spiritually, we must take the first step.

The Leap of Faith

Despite having some doubts, Soren Kierkegaard decided he would take that first step. He took what he called a "leap of faith" and began to live as if he believed. As a result, he became a sincere and passionate believer. The way you live your life shapes your belief system. Living by faith will gradually strengthen your faith. But the first step in the process is always action.

You act in faith all the time. You have faith that an airline pilot knows how to fly the plane you board and can bring it down safely. However, you can't be certain, can you? You get on that plane in faith. And the more you travel by plane, the greater your faith in air travel becomes.

As you live according to the teachings of your religion, you will move forward on the Path to spiritual enlightenment and wholeness. Once you take this leap and live by faith, you will probably find that your beliefs and your feelings will come into harmony with your new behavior; your doubts and misgivings will gradually be replaced by assurance and confidence.

If you are waiting for something of cosmic proportions to happen to you before you start your spiritual journey - forget it. It may never happen. Why wait for something which may never occur when you can do something today? Like most worthwhile endeavors in life, you have to be proactive not reactive when it comes to spiritual matters. As you walk toward Him, He walks toward you - double time. You don't have to become a "good" person before God will embrace you and come into a relationship with you. His desire is to use your talents. He wants to become your friend and partner. He'll accept you - warts and all - just the way you are.

The Joy of Your Embrace

The greatest biblical heroes were not perfect. In fact, most of them were not very nice. Jacob, the father of the 12 tribes of Israel, was a master of deception. Moses had killed a man and was on the run when God first spoke to him on Mount Sinai. When God commissioned Moses to go back into Egypt to help free the Hebrew people, Moses tried to convince God that he was not the right man for the job. King David was an adulterer and a murderer, yet God called David a "man after my own heart." (It may have been David's great faith, his zeal to do God's will and his sincere repentance whenever he sinned that earned David that accolade.) Peter, the disciple of Jesus, was an impulsive man who had a fierce temper. He swore his allegiance to Jesus and said he would die for his master. But when the Roman soldiers arrested Jesus and took him away, Peter denied that he ever knew him. It is a *myth* that God loves only the righteous. Yes, God will embrace you - just the way you are.

Behold, I stand at the door and knock; if anyone hears My voice and opens the door, I will come into him, and will dine with him, and he with Me.
                    - Revelation 3:20

You have heard it said that "God is just a crutch." I guess you can say that God *is* a crutch. Not only does He help those who help themselves, He also helps those who *can't* help themselves. But God is so much more. In a sense, God is also a "ladder," for it is life that is led by the spirit which allows us to climb to heights we can never reach without Him. He gives us a new set of eyes with which to see the world - eyes that allow us to navigate wisely through life.

Deciding to live a more spiritual existence will often feel like you are taking a leap into air, into the arms of the

Unknown. At times, it will not be easy. And because there is much you must learn, God will place you into difficult situations that require great strength, love, and endurance to overcome. But this Path, should you decide to walk it, will lead you to the most exciting adventure you could ever imagine. At the end, you will be able to say that your life had meaning.

So go ahead and act. Open the door to your soul. Exercise the faith you possess and change your life. Nourish your spirit and quench its thirst. As your spirit is strengthened, your mind and your body will also be empowered. Take that leap and boldly advance upon your journey. God is waiting. His arms are open wide and they await the joy of your embrace.

Then you will call upon Me and come and pray to Me, and I will listen to you. And you will seek Me and find Me, when you search for Me with all your heart.
　　　　　　　　　　　　　　-Jeremiah 29:12-13

✦✦✦✦✦✦✦✦

GOD'S SOLUTIONS
TO ALL YOUR PROBLEMS

The ancient writings in scripture provide inspiration, solace and guidance. And if you believe that the prophets were inspired by God to write these words, you can be assured that the Author has provided you with the ultimate prescription for personal development.

In **Part II**, you will find a collection of Bible verses which will assist you **enormously** in all areas of your life. After you read and reflect upon their meaning, *act* upon them. If you do, I can assure you that your life will unfold in ways you never dreamed possible.

NOTE: Some of the following verses have been paraphrased and written as an affirmation (when this is done, it will be so indicated with an **A** next to the Bible reference.)

✦✦✦✦✦✦✦✦

PART II

ANCIENT AFFIRMATIONS

Anger

He who is slow to anger has great understanding, but he who is quick-tempered exalts folly.   *- Proverbs 14:29*

For His anger is but for a moment, His favor is for a lifetime; weeping may last for the night, but a shout of joy comes in the morning.   *- Psalms 30:5*

I am quick to listen, slow to speak, and slow to anger; for the anger of man does not achieve the righteousness of God.   *- A. James 1:19*

Be angry, and yet do not sin; do not let the sun go down on your anger.   *- Ephesians 4:26*

A hot-tempered man stirs up strife, but the slow to anger pacifies contention.   *- Proverbs 15:18*

Anxiety

God is our refuge and strength, an ever present help in trouble.

Therefore we will not fear, though the earth give way and the mountains fall into the heart of the sea;

Though its waters roar and foam and the mountains quake with their surging.
- Psalms 46:1-3

He will call upon Me, and I will answer him; I will be with him in trouble, I will deliver him and honor him.
- Psalm 91:15

Cast your burden upon the Lord and He will sustain you; He will never allow the righteous to be shaken.
- Psalms 55:22

The Lord is my shepherd,
   I shall not want.
He makes me lie down in green pastures;
He leads me beside quiet waters.
He restores my soul;
He guides me in the paths of righteousness
For His name's sake.
- Psalms 23:1-3

Cast all your anxiety upon Him, because He cares for you.
- 1 Peter 5:7

I am not anxious for tomorrow; for tomorrow will care for itself. Each day has enough trouble of its own.

- A. Matthew 6:34

Comfort

Though I walk in the midst of trouble, Thou wilt revive me; Thou wilt stretch forth Thy hand against the wrath of my enemies; and Thy right hand will save me.   *- Psalms 138:7*

The Lord is good, a refuge in times of trouble.
He cares for those who trust in him.   *- Nahum 1:7*

Cast your cares on the Lord and He will sustain you; He will never let the righteous fall.   *- Psalms 55:22*

"Come to Me, all who are weary and heavy-laden and I will give you rest.

"Take My yoke upon you, and learn from Me, for I am gentle and humble in heart;

"For My yoke is easy, and My load is light."

- Matthew 11:28-30

Nevertheless I am continually with Thee; Thou hast taken hold of my right hand.

You guide me with Thy counsel, and afterward Thou wilt take me into glory.   *- Psalms 73:23-24*

I, I am He that comforts you; who are you that you are afraid of man who dies, of the son of man who is made like grass.

- Isaiah 51:12

Confidence

For the Lord will be your confidence, and will keep your foot from being caught.   *- Proverbs 3:26*

I am confident. For God has not given me a spirit of timidity, but a spirit of power, and love and discipline.
- A. 2 Timothy 1:7

The Lord is my light and my salvation; whom shall I fear? The Lord is the stronghold of my life; of whom Shall I be afraid?   *- Psalms 27:1*

Hence we can confidently say, "The Lord is my helper, I will not be afraid; what can man do to me?" *- Hebrews 13:6*

Contentment

A cheerful heart is good medicine, but a crushed spirit dries up the bones.   *- Proverbs 17:22*

Let your way of life be free from the love of money, being content with what you have; for He Himself has said,"I WILL NEVER DESERT YOU, NOR WILL I EVER FORSAKE YOU."   *- Hebrews 13:5*

"He will call upon Me, and I will answer him; I will be with him in times of trouble; I will rescue him and honor him."   *- Psalms 91:15*

All the days of the oppressed are wretched, but the cheerful heart has a continual feast.   *- Proverbs 15:15*

A heart at peace gives life to the body, but envy rots the bones.   *- Proverbs 14:30*

Courage

"Be strong and courageous! Do not tremble or be dismayed, for the Lord your God is with you wherever you go."   *- Joshua 1:9*

I am strong and I do not lose courage, for there is reward for my work.   *- A. 2 Chronicles 14:7*

You are my hiding place; you will protect me from trouble and surround me with songs of deliverance.   *- Psalms 32:7*

The Lord is my strength and my song; He has become my salvation.   *- Psalms 118:14*

God is my refuge and strength, a very present help in trouble. Therefore I will not fear though the earth should change, though the mountains shake in the heart of the sea.
- A. Psalms 46:1-2

Faith

What use is it, my brothers, if a man says he has faith, but he has no works? Can that faith save him? For just as the body without the spirit is dead, so also faith without works is dead.
- James 2:14,26

"Behold, as for the proud one, His soul is not right with him; but the righteous will live by his faith." *- Habakkuk 2:4*

Now faith is the assurance of things hoped for, the conviction of things not seen.   *- Hebrews 11:1*

And without faith it is impossible to please Him, for he who comes to God must believe that He is, and that He is a rewarder of those who seek Him.

- Hebrews 11:6

I consider it all joy, when I encounter various trials, knowing that the testing of my faith produces patience.
- A. James 1:2-3

Though the fig tree should not blossom, and there be no fruit on the vines, though the yield of the olive should fail, and the fields produce no food, though the flock should be cut off from the fold, and there be no cattle in the stalls,

Yet I will exult in the Lord, I will rejoice in the God of my salvation.

The Lord God is my strength, and He has made my feet like hinds' feet, and makes me walk on high places.
- Habakkuk 3:17-19

" ... if you have faith as a mustard seed, you shall say to this mountain, 'Move from here to there,' and it shall move; and nothing shall be impossible to you."
- Matthew 17:20b

Family Values

"Honor your father and your mother...."

- Exodus 20:12a

Train up a child in the way he should go, and even when he is old he will not depart from it.   *- Proverbs 22:6*

"It would be better for him if a millstone were hung around his neck and he were thrown into the sea, than that he should cause one of these little ones to stumble."   *- Luke 17:2*

A wise son makes a father glad. But a foolish son is a grief to his mother.   *- Proverbs 10:1*

Discipline your son while there is hope, and do not desire his death.   *- Proverbs 19:18*

Let marriage be held in honor among all, and let the marriage be undefiled; for fornicators and adulterers God will judge.   *- Hebrews 13:4*

And if a house is divided against itself, that house will not be able to stand.   *- Mark 3:25*

"And these words, which I am commanding you today, shall be on your heart;

and you shall *teach them diligently* to your sons and shall talk of them when you sit in your house and when you walk by the way and when you lie down and when you rise up."

- Deuteronomy 6:6-7

"Choose for yourselves today whom you will serve;... as for me and my house, we will serve the Lord."

- Joshua 24:15

An excellent wife, who can find? For her worth is far above jewels.

The heart of her husband trusts in her, and he will have no lack of gain.

She does him good and not evil all the days of her life.

Her children rise up and bless her; her husband also, and he praises her saying:

"Many daughters have done nobly, but you excel them all."

Charm is deceitful and beauty is vain, but a woman who fears the Lord, she shall be praised.

- Proverbs 31:10-12, 28-30

Children, obey your parents in the Lord, for this is right. And fathers, do not provoke your children to anger; but bring them up in the discipline and instruction of the Lord.

- Ephesians 6:1,4

Fear

When you lie down, you will not be afraid; when you lie down, your sleep will be sweet.   *- Proverbs 3:24*

"But whoever listens to me will live in safety and be at ease, without fear of harm."   *- Proverbs 1:33*

For I am the Lord, your God, who takes hold of your right hand and says to you, Do not fear; I will help you.
                                        - Isaiah 41:13

I do not fear those who kill the body but cannot kill the soul...
                                        - A. Matthew 10:28a

"For the eyes of the Lord are on the righteous and his ears are attentive to their prayer, but the face of the Lord is against those who do evil."

Who is going to harm you if you are eager to do good?

But even if you should suffer for what is right, you are blessed. "Do not fear what they fear; do not be frightened."
                                        - 1 Peter 3:12-14

Finding God

Call to Me, and I will answer you, and I will tell you great and mighty things, which you do not know. - *Jeremiah 33:3*

"But from there you will seek the Lord your God, and you will find *Him* if you search for Him with all your heart and all your soul."
                                                           - *Deuteronomy 4:29*

If My people who are called by My name humble themselves and pray, and seek My face and turn from their wicked ways, then I will hear from heaven, will forgive their sin, and will heal their land.

                                                           - *2 Chronicles 7:14*

I submit myself to You, O God. I resist Satan and he flees from me. As I come near to You, You come nearer to me.
                                                           - *A. James 4:7-8*

Jesus answered and said to him, "Truly, truly, I say to you, unless one is born again he cannot see the kingdom of God."
                                                           - *John 3:3*

"Seek the Lord while He may be found, call upon Him while He is near;
    let the wicked forsake his way, and the unrighteous man

his thoughts; let him return to the Lord, that He may have mercy on him, and to our God, for He will abundantly pardon.

For my thoughts are not your thoughts, neither are your ways my ways, says the Lord.

For as the heavens are higher than the earth, so are My ways higher than your ways and My thoughts than your thoughts."   *- Isaiah 55:6-9*

Then you will call upon Me and come and pray to Me, and I will listen to you.

And you will seek Me and find Me, when you search for Me with all your heart.   *- Jeremiah 29:12-13*

"Behold, I stand at the door and knock; if anyone hears My voice and opens the door, I will come into him, and will dine with him, and he with Me."   *- Revelation 3:20*

Seek the Lord and His strength;
Seek His face continually.   *- 1 Chronicles 16:11*

Forgiveness

For high as the heavens are above the earth, so great is His loving kindness toward those who fear Him.

As far as the east is from the west, so far has He removed our transgressions from us.   *- Psalms 103:11-12*

"For if you forgive men for their transgressions, your heavenly Father will also forgive you.

"But if you do not forgive men, then your Father will not forgive your transgressions."   *- Matthew 6:14-15*

Whenever I pray, if I have anything against anyone, I forgive him, so that my Father in heaven may forgive me my sins.

*- **A.** Mark 11:25*

"Come now, and let us reason together," says the Lord, "though your sins are as scarlet, they will be as white as snow; though they be as red as crimson, they will be like wool."

- Isaiah 1:18

Then Peter came and said to Him, "Lord, how often shall my brother sin against me and I forgive him? Up to seven times?"

Jesus said to him, "I do not say to you, up to seven times, but up to seventy times seven."   *- Matthew 18:21-22*

God's Love

I love all those who love Me, and those who diligently seek Me shall surely find Me.   *- Proverbs 8:17*

For as high as the heavens are from the earth, so great is His loving kindness toward those who fear Him.

- Psalms 103:11

The Lord is gracious and merciful; slow to anger and great in loving kindness.   *- Psalms 145:8*

The Lord is my strength and my shield; my heart trusts in Him, and I am helped; therefore my heart exults, and with my song I shall thank Him.   *- Psalms 28:7*

The Lord detests the way of the wicked but He loves those who pursue righteousness.   *- Proverbs 15:9*

The Lord gives sight to the blind, the Lord lifts up those who are bowed down, the Lord loves the righteous.

- Psalms 146:8

The Lord my God is with me, He is mighty to save. He will take great delight in me, He will quiet me with his love, He will rejoice over me with singing.   *- A. Zephaniah 3:17*

Guidance

"I will instruct you and teach you in the way in which you should go; I will counsel you with My eye upon you."
                                                            - Psalms 32:8

Whether you turn to the right or to the left, your ears will hear a voice behind you, saying, "this is the way; walk in it."
                                                            - Isaiah 30:21

For such is God, My God forever and ever; He will guide me until death.   *- **A.** Psalms 48:14*

Trust in the Lord with all your heart, and do not lean on your *own* understanding.

In all your ways acknowledge Him, and He will make your paths straight.   *- Proverbs 3:5-6*

But when He, the Spirit of truth comes, He will *guide* you into all truth; for He will not speak on His own initiative, but whatever He hears, He will speak; and He will disclose to you what is to come.   *- John 16:13*

Guilt

As far as the east is from the west, so far has He removed
my transgressions from me.   *- A. Psalms 103:12*

If we confess our sins, He is faithful and just and will
forgive us our sins and purify us from all unrighteousness.
                                          - 1 John 1:9

"I, even I, am He who blots out your transgressions, for my
own sake, and remembers your sins no more." *- Isaiah 43:25*

Let the wicked forsake his way and the evil man his
thoughts. Let him turn to the Lord, and He will have mercy on
him, and to our God, for He will freely pardon. *- Isaiah 55:7*

"For I will forgive their wickedness and will remember
their sins no more."   *- Hebrews 8:12*

I will cleanse them from all the sin they have committed
against Me and will forgive all their sins of rebellion against
Me.   *- Jeremiah 33:8*

Health

A heart at peace gives life to the body, but envy rots the bones.
- Proverbs 14:30

Do not be wise in your own eyes; fear the Lord and turn away from evil.

It will be a healing to your body, and refreshment to your bones.
- Proverbs 3:7-8

"But I will restore you to health and heal your wounds," declares the Lord.
- Jeremiah 30:17

Heal me, O Lord, and I will be healed; save me and I will be saved, for you are the one I praise.
- Jeremiah 17:14

A cheerful heart is good medicine, but a crushed spirit dries up the bones.
- Proverbs 17:22

Helping Others

And if you give yourself to the hungry, and satisfy the desire of the afflicted, then your light will rise in the darkness, and your gloom will become like midday.
- Isaiah 58:10

"But when you give alms, do not let your left hand know what your right hand is doing,

that your alms may be in secret; and your Father who sees in secret will repay you."   *- Matthew 6:3-4*

When I give, I do so from my heart; not grudgingly or under compulsion; for God loves a cheerful giver.

*- **A.** 2 Corinthians 9:7*

"Give, and it will be given to you; good measure, pressed down, shaken together, running over, they will pour into your lap. For what measure you deal out to others, it will be dealt to you in return."   *- Luke 6:38*

Dear children, let us not love with words or tongue but with actions and in truth.   *- 1 John 3:18*

Hope

And let us not lose heart in doing good, for in due time, we shall reap if we do not grow weary.   *- Galatians 6:9*

I am strong, and my heart takes courage, for my hope is in the Lord.   *- **A.** Psalms 31:24*

My soul, wait in silence for God only, for my hope is from Him.

He alone is my rock and my salvation, my stronghold; I shall not be shaken.   *- Psalms 62:5-6*

Though He slay me, I will hope in Him. Nevertheless, I will argue my ways before Him.   *- Job 13:15*

When calamity comes, the wicked are brought down, but even in death the righteous have a refuge.   *- Proverbs 14:32*

The Lord gives sight to the blind, the Lord lifts up those who are bowed down, the Lord loves the righteous.

- Psalms 146:8

Joy

Thou wilt make known to me, the path of life; in Thy presence is fullness of joy; in Thy right hand there are pleasures forever.

- Psalms 16:11

Shout for joy, O heavens! And rejoice, O earth! Break forth into joyful shouting, O mountains! For the Lord has comforted His people, and will have compassion on His afflicted.

- Isaiah 49:13

"For I will go out with joy, and I will be led forth with peace; the mountains and the hills will break forth into shouts of joy before me, and all the trees of the field will clap their hands."   *- A. Isaiah 55:12*

"Blessed is the man who trusts in the Lord, and whose trust is the Lord.

"For he will be like a tree planted by the water, that extends its roots by a stream, and will not fear when the heat comes; but its leaves will be green, and it will not be anxious in a year of drought nor cease to yield fruit."

- Jeremiah 17:7-8

Though I have not seen Him, I love Him, and though I do not see Him now, but believe in Him, I greatly rejoice with joy inexpressible and full of glory.   *- A. 1 Peter 1:8*

"These things I have spoken to you, that My joy may be in you, and that your joy may be made full.

"This is My commandment, that you love one another, just as I have loved you."   *- John 15:11-12*

Love for One Another

Teacher, what is the greatest commandment in the Law?
And He said to him, " 'YOU SHALL LOVE THE LORD YOUR GOD WITH ALL YOUR HEART, AND WITH ALL

YOUR SOUL, AND WITH ALL YOUR MIND.
"This is the great and foremost commandment.
"And a second is like it, 'YOU SHALL LOVE YOUR NEIGHBOR AS YOURSELF.' "

- Matthew 22:35-39

Dear children, let us not love only with words or tongue but with actions and in truth.   *- 1 John 3:18*

Love is patient, love is kind, and is not jealous; love does not brag and is not arrogant,
does not act unbecomingly; it does not seek its own, is not provoked, does not take into account a wrong suffered,
does not rejoice in unrighteousness, but rejoices with the truth;
bears all things, hopes all things, endures all things.
Love never fails.

- 1 Corinthians 13:4-8a

There is no fear in love; but perfect love casts out fear.
- 1 John 4:18

Whoever loves his brother lives in the light, and there is nothing in him to make him stumble.   *- 1 John 2:10*

Overcoming Fear

The Lord is for me I am not afraid; what can man do to me?
- A. Matthew 10:28a

The fear of man brings a snare, but he who trusts in the Lord will be exalted.
- Proverbs 29:25

Even though I walk through the valley of the shadow of death, I fear no evil; for Thou art with me; Thy rod and Thy staff, they comfort me.
- Psalms 23:4

God is my refuge and my strength, a very present help in trouble.
- A. Psalms 46:1

Because I listen to You, O God, I live in safety, I am at ease without fear of harm.
- A. Proverbs 1:33

Thank you Lord for being an ever-present source of strength. When I lie down, I am not afraid; when I lie down, my sleep is sweet.
- A. Proverbs 3:24

For I am the Lord your God, who upholds your right hand, who says to you, "Do not fear, I will help you."

- Isaiah 41:13

Overcoming Temptation

Do not love the world, nor the things in the world. If anyone loves the world, the love of the Father is not in him.

For all that is in the world, the lust of the flesh and the lust of the eyes and the boastful pride of life, is not from the Father, but is from the world.

- 1 John 2:15-16

Let no one say when he is tempted, "I am being tempted by God"; for God cannot be tempted by evil, and He Himself does not tempt anyone.

But each one is tempted when he is carried away and enticed by his own lust.

Then when lust has conceived, it gives birth to sin; and when sin is accomplished, it brings forth death.

- James 1:13-15

Submit therefore to God. Resist the devil and he will flee from you.

Draw near to God and He will draw near to you.

- James 4:7-8a

God is faithful, and will not allow me to be tempted beyond what I am able, but with the temptation will provide the way of escape also, that I may be able to endure it.

- A. 1 Corinthians 10:13

Patience and Endurance

And let us not lose heart in doing good, for in due time, we shall reap if we do not grow weary.

- Galatians 6:9

There is an appointed time for everything. And there is a time for every event under heaven.

A time to weep, and a time to laugh; a time to mourn and a time to dance.

- Ecclesiastes 3:1,4

Consider it all joy, my brethren, when you encounter trials, knowing that the testing of your faith produces endurance.

And let endurance have its perfect result, that you may be perfect and complete, lacking in nothing.

- James 1:2-4

Wait for the Lord, be strong, and let your heart take courage; yea, wait for the Lord!

- Psalms 27:14

Peace

Because my mind is fixed on You, O Lord, I have perfect peace; I trust in You.

- A. Isaiah 26:3

Lord, You faithfully give me your peace; you do not give it as the world gives. My heart is without trouble and I am not afraid.

- A. John 14:27

"These things I have spoken to you, that in Me you have peace. In the world you have tribulation, but take courage, I have overcome the world."

- John 16:33

"Peace I leave with you; My peace I give to you; not as the world gives, do I give to you. Let not your heart be troubled, nor let it be afraid."

- John 14:27

The fruit of righteousness will be peace; the effect of righteousness will be quietness and confidence forever.

- Isaiah 32:17

Even though I walk through the valley of the shadow of
    death, I will fear no evil; for Thou art with me.

Thy rod and Thy staff, they comfort me.

Thou dost prepare a table before me in the presence of my
    enemies;

Thou hast anointed my head with oil;

My cup overflows.

- Psalms 23:4,5

Positive Thinking

As a man thinks within himself, so is he.

- Proverbs 23:7a

Whatever is true, whatever is honorable, whatever is right,
whatever is pure, whatever is lovely, whatever is of good
repute, if anything is worthy of praise, let your mind dwell on
these things.   *- Philippians 4:8*

"Son of man, look with your eyes, and hear with your ears,
and set your mind upon all that I shall show you..."

- Ezekiel 40:4a

Thou dost keep him in perfect peace, whose mind is stayed
on Thee, because he trusts in Thee.   *- Isaiah 26:3*

Praising God (Brings Peace and Joy)

Praise the Lord! How blessed is the man who fears the Lord, Who greatly delights in His commandments.

His descendants will be mighty on earth; the generation of the upright will be blessed.

Wealth and riches are in his house, And his righteousness endures forever.   *- Psalms 112:1-3*

Praise the Lord! Praise, O servants of the Lord. Praise the name of the Lord.

Blessed be the name of the Lord from this time forth and forever.

From the rising of the sun to its setting the name of the Lord is to be praised.

The Lord is high above all nations; His glory is above the heavens.   *- Psalms 113:1-4*

Praise the Lord! Praise the Lord from the heavens; Praise Him in the heights!

Praise Him all His angels; Praise Him all His hosts!

Praise Him, sun and moon; Praise Him, all stars of light!
                    - Psalms 148:1-4

Praise the Lord! Praise Him in His sanctuary; Praise Him in His mighty expanse.

Praise Him for His mighty deeds; Praise Him according to His excellent greatness.

Let everything that has breath praise the Lord. Praise the Lord!   *- Psalms 150:1-2,6*

Prayer

"And without faith it is impossible to please Him, for He who comes to God must believe that He is, and that He is a rewarder of those who seek Him."

- Hebrews 11:6

"Truly I say to you, whoever says to this mountain, 'Be taken up and cast into the sea,' and does not doubt in his heart but believes that what he says is going to happen, it shall be granted him.

"Therefore, I say to you, all things for which you pray and ask, believe that you have received them, and they shall be granted you." *- Mark 11:23-24*

You ask and do not receive, because you ask with wrong motives, so that you may spend it on your pleasures.

- James 4:3

Is anyone among you suffering? Let him pray. Is anyone cheerful? Let him sing praises. The prayer of a righteous man has great power in its effects. *- James 5:13a,16b*

"And I say to you, ask, and it shall be given to you; seek and you shall find; knock and it shall be opened to you.

"For everyone who asks, receives; and he who seeks, finds; and to him who knocks, it shall be opened." *- Luke 11:9,10*

Pride

A man's pride will bring him low, but a humble spirit will obtain honor.   *- Proverbs 29:23*

"For from within, out of the heart of men, proceed the evil thoughts and fornications, thefts, murders, adulteries,

deeds of coveting and wickedness, as well as deceit, sensuality, envy, slander, pride and foolishness.

"All these evil things proceed from within and defile the man."

- Mark 7:21-23

I let others praise me, and not myself; I let strangers, but never my own lips.   *- A. Proverbs 27:2*

Do you see a man wise in his own eyes? There is more hope for a fool than for him.   *- Proverbs 26:12*

"You hypocrite, first take the log out of your own eye, and then you will see clearly enough to take the speck out of your brother's eye."   *- Matthew 7:5*

"But the greatest among you shall be your servant.

"And whoever exalts himself shall be humbled; and whoever humbles himself shall be exalted."

- Matthew 23:11-12

"But many who are first shall be last; and the last shall be first." *- Matthew 19:30*

Rewards

Every good thing bestowed and every perfect gift is from above, coming down from the Father of lights, with whom there is no variation, or shifting shadow. *- James 1:17*

"And I say to you, *ask* and it shall be given to you; *seek* and you shall find; *knock* and it shall be opened to you.

"For everyone who asks, receives; and he who seeks, finds; and to him who knocks, it shall be opened." *- Luke 11:9,10*

Delight yourself in the Lord; and He will give you the desires of your heart.

Commit your way to the Lord, trust also in Him, and He will do it. *- Psalms 37:4-5*

He will fulfill the desire of those who fear Him, He will also hear their cry and will save them.

The Lord keeps all who love Him; but all the wicked, He will destroy.   *- Psalms 145:19-20*

Surely then I will find delight in the Almighty and will lift up my face to God.   *- Job 22:26*

Sin

"The heart is more deceitful than all else
 And is desperately sick;
 Who can understand it?"   *- Jeremiah 17:9*

Therefore, to one who knows the right thing to do, and does not do it, to him it is sin.   *- James 4:17*

"Keep watching and praying, that you may not come into temptation; the spirit is willing, but the flesh is weak."
                          - Mark 14:38

I will sprinkle clean water on you, and you will be clean; I will cleanse you from all your impurities and from all your idols.

I will give you a new heart and put a new spirit in you; I will remove from you your heart of stone and give you a heart of flesh.

- Ezekiel 36:25,26

"And this is the judgement, that the light is come into the world, and men loved the darkness rather than the light; for their deeds were evil.

"For everyone who desires evil hates the light, and does not come to the light, lest his deeds should be exposed.

"But he who practices the truth comes to the light..."

- John 3:19-21a

Spiritual Growth

"And the Lord will continually guide you, and satisfy your desire in scorched places, and give strength to your bones; and you will be like a watered garden, and like a spring of water whose waters do not fail."

- Isaiah 58:11

While we look not at the things that are seen, but at the things which are not seen; for the things which are seen are temporal, but the things which are not seen are eternal.

- 2 Corinthians 4:18

But someone may *well* say, "You have faith, and I have works; show me your faith without the works, and I will show you my faith by my works."

You see that a man is justified by works, and not by faith alone.

For just as the body without the spirit is dead, so also faith without works is dead.

- James 2:18,24,26

"Do not marvel that I said to you, 'You must be born again'.

"The wind blows where it wishes and you hear the sound of it, but do not know where it comes from and where it is going; so is every one who is born of the Spirit."

- John 3:7-8

Strength

God gives strength to the weary, and to him who lacks might He increases power.   *- Isaiah 40:29*

Yet those who wait for the Lord will gain new strength, they will mount up with wings like eagles, they will run and not get tired, they will walk and not become weary.

- Isaiah 40:31

The way of the Lord is a stronghold to the upright, but ruin to the workers of iniquity.   *- Proverbs 10:29*

Finally, be strong in the Lord, and in the strength of His might.

Put on the full armor of God, that you may be able to stand firm against the schemes of the devil.

- Ephesians 6:10-11

Even though I walk through the valley of
   the shadow of death,
I fear no evil; for Thou art with me.
Thy rod and Thy staff, they comfort me.

- Psalms 23:4

$\mathscr{S}uccess$

Humility and fear of the Lord bring wealth
and honor and life.   *- Proverbs 22:4*

With me are riches and honor, enduring wealth and prosperity.

My fruit is better than fine gold; what I yield surpasses choice silver.   *- Proverbs 8:18,19*

The house of the righteousness contains great treasure, but the income of the wicked brings them trouble.

- Proverbs 15:6

Blessed is the man who walks not in the counsel of the wicked, nor stands in the way of sinners, nor sits in the seat of scoffers.

He is like a tree planted by streams of water, that yields its fruit in its season, and its leaf does not wither. In all that he does, he prospers.   *- Psalms 1:1,3*

Thankfulness

O come, let us sing for joy to the Lord; let us shout joyfully to the rock of our salvation.

Let us come before His presence with thanksgiving; let us shout joyfully to Him with psalms.

For the Lord is a great God, and a great king above all gods.   *- Psalms 95:1-3*

Know that the Lord Himself is God; it is He who has made us, and not we ourselves; we are His people and the sheep of His pasture.

Enter His gates with thanksgiving, and His courts with praise. Give thanks to Him; bless His name.

- Psalms 100:3-4

O give thanks to the Lord, for *He* is good; For His loving kindness is everlasting.

- 1 Chronicles 16:34

Oh give thanks to the Lord, call upon His name;
Make known His deeds among the peoples.
                                        - 1 Chronicles 16:8

Victory over Trials

And I know that God causes all things to work together for good to those who love Him, and are called according to His purpose.   *- A. Romans 8:28*

By your perseverance you will win your souls.
                                        - Luke 21:19

"And as for you, you meant evil against me, but God meant it for good in order to bring about this present result..."
                                        - Genesis 50:20a

My son, do not reject the discipline of the Lord, or loathe His reproof,
For whom the Lord loves He reproves, even as a father, the son in whom He delights.   *- Proverbs 3:11-12*

Blessed is a man who perseveres under trial; for once he has been approved, he will receive the crown of life, which the Lord has promised to those who love Him.   *- James 1:12*

"Those whom I love, I reprove and discipline; be zealous therefore, and repent."   *- Revelation 3:19*

When Trouble Comes

The Lord is good, a refuge in times of trouble; He cares for me because I trust in Him.

- A. Nahum 1:7

Thou art my hiding place; Thou preserves me from trouble; Thou dost surround me with songs of deliverance. [Selah].

- Psalms 32:7

My flesh and my heart may fail; but God is the strength of my heart and my portion forever.

For, behold, those who are far from Thee will perish; Thou hast destroyed all those who are unfaithful to Thee.

- Psalms 73:26-27

"Come to Me, all who are weary and heavy-laden, and I will give you rest.

"Take My yoke upon you, and learn from Me, for I am gentle and humble in heart; and YOU SHALL FIND REST FOR YOUR SOULS.

"For My yoke is easy, and My load is light."

- Matthew 11:28-30

The Lord sustains all who fall, and raises up all who are bowed down.

- Psalms 145:14

Wisdom

The law of the Lord is perfect, restoring the soul; the testimony of the Lord is sure, making wise the simple.

- Psalms 19:7

The fear of the Lord is the beginning of knowledge; fools despise wisdom and instruction.   *- Proverbs 1:7*

But if any of you lacks wisdom, let him ask of God, who gives to all men generously and without reproach, and it will be given to him.

But let him ask in faith without any doubting, for the one who doubts is like the surf of the sea driven and tossed by the wind.   *- James 1:5-6*

The wisdom from above is first pure, then peaceable, gentle, reasonable, full of mercy and good fruits, unwavering, and without hypocrisy.   *- James 3:17*

Thus says the Lord, "Let not a wise man boast of his wisdom, and let not the mighty man boast of his might, let not a rich man boast of his riches;

but let him who boasts boast of this, that he understands and knows Me, that I am the Lord who exercises loving kindness, justice, and righteousness on earth; for I delight in these things," declares the Lord.   *- Jeremiah 9:23,24*

"If you abide in My word, then you are
truly disciples of Mine;
    and you shall know the truth, and the
truth shall make you free."   *- John 8:31b-32*

✦✦✦✦✦✦✦✦

Index

ORDER FORM

Manna for a Modern Age

Price per book:
$14.95 + $4.00 shipping/handling   **Total: $18.95**

You may order by:
   Telephone: 1-800-431-1579
   Fax: 1-914-835-0398
   E-mail: Bookch@aol.com
   Mail: See below

Payment:

Check___   Payable to: *Book Clearing House*

                        Send check to: Book Clearing House
                                                46 Purdy Street
                                                Harrison, New York 10528

Credit Card___
        Master Card____   VISA____   Discover____   AMEX____

Card Number: _____

Full Name on Card (please print):
_____Exp. Date: ____/___

ORDER FORM

Manna for a Modern Age

Price per book:
$14.95 + $4.00 shipping/handling   **Total: $18.95**

You may order by:
    Telephone: 1-800-431-1579
    Fax: 1-914-835-0398
    E-mail: Bookch@aol.com
    Mail: See below

Payment:

Check___   Payable to: *Book Clearing House*

                 Send check to: Book Clearing House
                                   46 Purdy Street
                                   Harrison, New York 10528

Credit Card___
        Master Card____   VISA____   Discover____   AMEX____

Card Number: _____

Full Name on Card (please print):
_____Exp. Date: ____/____